CAMBRIDGE MONOGRAPHS IN
EXPERIMENTAL BIOLOGY

No. 4

EDITORS:
M. ABERCROMBIE, P. B. MEDAWAR
GEORGE SALT (*General Editor*)
M. M. SWANN, V. B. WIGGLESWORTH

THE
PHYSIOLOGY OF DIAPAUSE
IN ARTHROPODS

THE SERIES

Other volumes in preparation

To refer the hybernation of insects to the mere direct influence of cold, is to suppose one of the most important acts of their existence given up to the blind guidance of feelings which in the variable climates of Europe would be leading them into perpetual and fatal errors... It is not, we may rest assured, to such a deceptious guide that the Creator has entrusted the safety of so important a part of his creatures.

W. KIRBY and W. SPENCE, *An Introduction to Entomology* (1815)

THE
PHYSIOLOGY OF DIAPAUSE
IN ARTHROPODS

BY

A. D. LEES

M.A., PH.D.

Agricultural Research Council,
Unit of Insect Physiology, Cambridge

CAMBRIDGE
AT THE UNIVERSITY PRESS
1955

PUBLISHED BY
THE SYNDICS OF THE CAMBRIDGE UNIVERSITY PRESS

London Office: Bentley House, N.W. I
American Branch: New York

Agents for Canada, India and Pakistan: Macmillan

Printed in Great Britain at the University Press, Cambridge
(Brooke Crutchley, University Printer)

CONTENTS

v

Contents

ACKNOWLEDGEMENTS

Without the many stimulating discussions I have enjoyed with Dr T. O. Browning and Prof. Carroll M. Williams the planning of the present monograph would have proved more difficult. I am also indebted to Mr E. O. Pearson for the data contained in Fig. 14, to Dr E. H. Slifer for the sketch upon which Fig. 16 is based and to Dr H. E. Hinton for the loan of Fig. 18. Many authors have also permitted me to refer to unpublished work. This debt is acknowledged in the text. Finally, my thanks are due to Dr C. B. Goodhart for his kindness in translating many Russian papers.

A. D. L.

CAMBRIDGE
November, 1954

LIST OF TEXT-FIGURES

ix

List of Text-figures

CHAPTER I

INTRODUCTION

THE possession of a definitive 'resting stage' is a common feature in organisms that inhabit inconstant environments. In such forms of life the dormant state is usually characterized by the temporary failure of growth or reproduction, by the reduced metabolism and often by the enhanced resistance to adverse climatic factors such as cold, heat and drought. The appearance of the 'resting stage' may sometimes be evoked by just those conditions which it is adapted to survive. But the relationship is often more complex, for dormancy may supervene before the milieu becomes unfavourable for growth and sometimes persists after these conditions have vanished.

Although the occurrence of this state of arrested growth or diapause (διάπαυσις = rest, interruption of work) is particularly frequent in the Arthropoda, it is by no means confined to this group. In the plant kingdom many seeds, bulbs and the buds of woody plants display a similar type of dormancy. The gemmules of sponges, the yolky winter eggs of Cladocera and the drought-resisting eggs of *Artemia* and other branchiopod Crustacea, are all familiar examples of resting stages. Among the Vertebrata an excellent instance of diapause is afforded by the delayed implantation of the blastocyst in mammals such as the American marten and armadillo. Dormancy also occurs in the adult vertebrate. Sometimes the suspension of physiological activity is general, as in the hibernating marmot or aestivating *Protopterus*; sometimes, as in many birds and mammals, the growth failure is limited to the reproductive organs. Nevertheless, despite the generality of the phenomenon, it is perhaps not without significance that it is among the Insecta—a group in which normal growth is essentially discontinuous—that examples are most numerous and varied.

The ecological aspects of diapause have been stressed in the recent reviews of Bonnemaison (1945) and Andrewartha (1952). This condition has been rightly regarded as an important adaptation for preserving the species in regions where seasonal climatic conditions are unfavourable for continuous multi-plication. However, from the standpoint of physiology the central issue concerns the problem of growth and its control by intrinsic and extrinsic factors. It is now well known that both the arrest of growth itself and the accompanying metabolic adjustments are governed by the organs of internal secretion. These endocrine centres are in turn responsive to certain definite stimuli from the environment. Indeed, it is this link that per-mits the diapause mechanism to function as a timing device, synchronizing the periods of dormancy and active growth with the rhythm of the environment in general. These subjects will furnish the principal themes in the present monograph.

DEFINITION OF DIAPAUSE AND QUIESCENCE

The term diapause was introduced by Wheeler (1893) to describe a stage in the embryogenesis of the grasshopper *Xiphidium ensiferum*. The complicated pendulum-like movements of the embryo round the posterior pole of the egg were divided into an ascending stage (*anatrepsis*), when the embryo was moving tail-first through the yolk, and a descending stage (*catatrepsis*), when the direction of movement was reversed. All the movements were collectively referred to as *blastokinesis*. The phase intervening between anatrepsis and catatrepsis when the embryo remained poised with the head directed towards the posterior pole was called 'the diapause'.

The term was subsequently given an entirely different meaning by Henneguy (1904), who applied it not to a *stage* of morphogenesis but to the *condition* of arrested growth, whether in the developing or in the adult insect. Many authors have followed Henneguy in extending the term to cover all forms of arrested growth, even simple inhibition by cold. Yet as early as 1869 Duclaux had shown in experiments on the hibernating egg of the silkworm that the condition differs fundamentally from one of cold torpor. Duclaux observed that the egg batches of

2

Bombyx mori invariably failed to hatch at room temperatures, and eventually died, whereas similar batches which were first chilled for 40 days in an ice box hatched successfully when returned to the higher temperature.

In view of these special attributes, attempts have been made from time to time to frame a narrower definition of diapause. Thus Shelford (1929) suggested that the use of the term should be restricted to instances where development or activity is arrested 'spontaneously', whereas an interruption of growth directly controlled by unfavourable conditions could be referred to as quiescence. The terms 'diapause vrai' and 'pseudo-diapause' coined by Roubaud (1930) were based on similar distinctions.

Shelford's definition is perhaps no longer wholly appropriate, for in many cases the causes for the onset of diapause can be traced back to the action of the environment, although it is 'spontaneous' in the sense that the response may later become independent of the primary stimulus. However, the immediacy of the response to the environmental factor remains a valid basis for distinction, particularly if this factor is temperature. In the absence of a full experimental analysis, the type of arrest is usually classified more simply by reference to the termination of dormancy. For example, one insect will develop without delay when the temperature is 'favourable' for morphogenesis, whereas a second fails to develop (as in *Bombyx*) or grows slowly and irregularly. The recognition of these states as 'quiescence' and 'diapause' serves as a useful reminder that certain physiological mechanisms are brought into action in the diapausing insect which are absent in the quiescent—this is the implication of the delay which ensues before growth is resumed. The retention of these terms is further justified on the grounds of generality, since the termination of diapause in the vast majority of insects is controlled by temperature.

The distinction, however, is less clear when stimuli other than temperature govern the resumption of growth. The following example illustrates some of the difficulties. Researches by Gayspitz (1949, 1953) have shown that the larvae of the moth *Dendrolimus pini* (Lasiocampidae) will feed and grow without interruption at 19–20° C. provided they are continuously

I-2

illuminated. But if the day length is reduced to 9 hours per day the larvae moult once and finally become dormant within 30 days. In this state of dormancy, which persists for at least a month if the conditions are unchanged, feeding is spasmodic and the growth of the batches slow and uneven. However, the arrest can be ended at any time by exposure to continuous illumination; feeding and growth are then resumed after a delay of about 14 days.

Photoperiod is a stimulus which, unlike temperature, cannot be regarded as immediately favourable or unfavourable. Further, larval development in *Dendrolimus* is evidently more or less directly controlled by photoperiod; yet the definite time lag separating the institution of the new day-length régime and the response suggests that physiological changes of some complexity are set in motion by the stimulus. On these grounds it would be more justifiable to regard this as an instance of diapause.

There are other borderline examples. The ichneumonid parasite *Diplazon fissorius* will develop no further than the 1st instar until the syrphid host forms the puparium. By injecting larvae into developing hosts Schneider (1950) has proved that the parasite is activated almost instantly—probably by some change in the host's blood associated with pupation. This arrest is therefore more appropriately regarded as quiescence. In many insect larvae the absorption of water is a necessary prerequisite for the resumption of growth (see Chapter 5). Since the arrest is usually ended in a few days when water is made available, this too can be regarded as quiescence. However, it may well be that hydration influences growth through the endocrine system rather than by activating the tissues directly. In this event the final cause of the arrest, and of the resumption of growth, is internal to the insect, as it is in diapause. It is clearly inadvisable to press these distinctions too far. Even exposure to low temperature may influence the growth of the insect both directly, by inducing torpor, and indirectly by causing subtle changes in the hormone balance (Wigglesworth, 1952).

In classifying undoubted examples of diapause, the terminology introduced by Steinberg and Kamensky (1936) has proved of considerable utility. In many insects the potentialities for diapause are not realized in each generation. Diapause is then said to be facultative. The onset of the arrest in these species seems invariably to be influenced by the environment and can either be induced or averted by the appropriate external conditions. Other insects possess an obligatory diapause. When they are reared under varied conditions virtually every individual enters diapause in each generation regardless of the environment. Insects with facultative diapause commonly complete two or more generations annually in nature, while those with obligatory diapause exhibit a strictly univoltine* life cycle.

THE DIAPAUSE STAGES

Diapause may occur in any of the major stages of the life history. In the egg, larva or pupa it takes the form of an arrest of development; in the imago the state is associated with the failure to enlarge the reproductive organs, particularly the ovaries, and with the compensating hypertrophy of the fat body and other storage tissues. This process has been termed 'gonotrophic dissociation' by the students of mosquito physiology, but it is equally characteristic of all insects with an imaginal diapause.

The precise morphogenetic stage of the growth arrest in the egg or larva is also characteristic of the species. Growth may be halted when the embryo is still rudimentary, when it is half-grown, or when the young larva is fully formed but still unhatched (see p. 7). Larval arrests are perhaps most frequent in the last instar after the feeding period is ended; but many insects (for example, the Lepidoptera *Arctia caja, Lasiocampa quercus*) hibernate in the middle instars. In a few species such as the ermine moth *Hyponomeuta padella* (Thorpe, 1929) and the spruce budworm *Cacoecia* (*Choristoneura*) *fumiferana* (Graham and Orr, 1940) diapause supervenes immediately after the 1st-instar larva has hatched from the egg.

Although a general trend can be traced in some groups, the stage of arrest, even among closely related species, is often

---

* The term 'voltinism' derives from Italian sericulture: *volta* = time, in the sense of 'occasion'.

notably inconstant. For example, the tortricid *Cacoecia rosana* enters diapause as an egg, *C. fumiferana* as a newly emerged larva. The silkmoth *Antheraea yamamai* has an egg diapause, *A. pernyi* a pupal diapause. The multivoltine syrphid *Epistrophe balteata* possesses a facultative imaginal diapause, whereas the univoltine species *E. bifasciata* enters diapause at the close of the last larval stadium (Schneider, 1948).

These considerations suggest first, that diapause has often been evolved independently, and secondly, that in short-lived insects the selective value of this character is little affected by the stage in which it occurs. It is noteworthy that in insects with an imaginal life extending over several years, such as the beetle *Dytiscus marginalis*, diapause is of the reproductive type.

Although the point of occurrence of diapause within the life cycle is normally a very constant specific feature, larval arrests are sometimes influenced by temperature. If the Japanese beetle *Popillia japonica* is reared at 25° C. the 3rd instar is of relatively long duration, lasting for 126 days instead of the 92 days required at lower temperatures. At 20° C. growth is delayed in the 2nd or 3rd instar and at 17·5° C. in the 1st instar (Ludwig, 1932). Similarly, in *Orgyia gonostigma* (Lymantriidae) dormancy supervenes in the 5th and last instar at 22–25° C., in the 4th instar at 14–18° C., and in the 3rd instar at 10° C. (Kozhantshikov, 1948). High temperatures also cause the stage of arrest to be postponed to a later instar in the bug *Reduvius personatus* (Readio, 1931).

Although diapause is usually confined to one stage in the life cycle, there are a few exceptions. Both the pupa and egg of the winter moth *Operophtera brumata* are said to possess an obligatory diapause (Kozhantshikov, 1950*b*). In some insects with a facultative diapause, growth may be suspended in more than one instar. Development can be arrested in both the 3rd and the 6th instars of *Dendrolimus pini* if the 2nd and 5th instars are exposed to short photoperiods; indeed, the larva of this species sometimes overwinters twice in the northern part of its range (Gayspitz, 1949). In *Reduvius* all nymphs diapausing in the 3rd instar also experience a lengthy arrest in the 5th instar; and one-quarter of the nymphs which enter diapause in the 4th instar again become dormant in the 5th. In this insect it seems that the onset of diapause to some extent prevents the recurrence of the arrest in the succeeding instar (Readio, 1931).

The grasshopper *Pardalophora apiculata* has a two-year life cycle in western Canada, spending the first winter in the egg stage and the second as a late nymph. The eggs are of the diapause type and probably the overwintering nymphs also exhibit this condition as they fail to grow even at high temperatures (Pickford, 1953). Other insects requiring two years for development have a definitive diapause stage only in the last larval stadium, the first winter being passed in quiescence as a half-grown larva. Two examples are the alder fly *Sialis lutaria* (Rahm, 1952) and the dragonfly *Anax imperator* (Corbet, 1954).

THE STAGES OF ARREST IN EMBRYONIC DIAPAUSE

In the post-embryonic stages of insects the cyclical nature of ecdysis and growth may well favour the evolution of diapause mechanisms. This 'predisposition' is less apparent in the embryo where morphogenesis is continuous. Nevertheless, a closer examination suggests that the arrests are confined to certain definite periods in the growth and differentiation of the embryo.

From this point of view it is convenient to divide embryonic development into three stages. The first phase sees the successive divisions of the cleavage nuclei and ends with the formation of the blastoderm. The second includes the early growth of the embryo up to the beginning of the formation of the mesoderm. This phase, which corresponds approximately to anatrepsis, is one of growth but not of differentiation. The number of cells in the embryo is increased by mitosis, the somites are blocked out and the rudiments of the appendages appear, but all the cells remain alike in form. During the third phase, which commences at the beginning of catatrepsis, active growth and cellular differentiation proceed side by side. By the end of catatrepsis all the main organ systems have been differentiated. Fig. 1 illustrates the changes in the external morphology of an insect with embryonic diapause, namely, the cricket *Gryllulus commodus*.

No species are known in which diapause supervenes before the formation of the blastoderm. The arrest occurs immediately after this point in the winter egg of the fruit-tree red spider mite *Metatetranychus ulmi*, for no definitive germ band has been distinguished with certainty. In the grasshopper *Austroicetes*

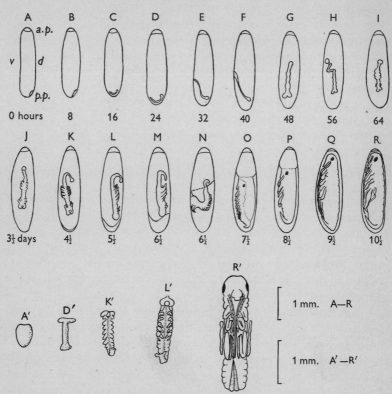

Fig. 1. Embryonic development in *Gryllulus commodus* (after Brookes). A–R, stages reached during blastokinesis at an incubation temperature of 25° C. A′–R′, changes in the form of the embryo at corresponding time intervals. A–K, anatrepsis. L–R, catatrepsis. From A to F the embryo is moving tail-first round the posterior pole of the egg and sinking into the yolk. If the egg is affected by diapause the arrest occurs at stage J. Rupture of the amnio-serosal membrane and the revolution of the embryo occur at stages M and N. Dorsal closure is complete by stage Q. *a.p.*, *p.p.* anterior and posterior poles; *d*, dorsal; *v*, ventral.

cruciata development is only a little further advanced when diapause sets in. The first rudiment of the embryo is nevertheless visible as a small cap of cells formed by the condensation of the blastoderm (Steele, 1941). The eggs of some Lepidoptera

Introduction

(*Notolophus thyellina, Dendrolimus undans excellans, Archips xylosteanus*) and a cricket *Homeogryllus japonica* are also known to enter diapause at this early stage of embryogenesis (fig. 2 A, B) (Umeya, 1950).

In some species growth may cease at a slightly later stage when the embryo is dumbbell-shaped but as yet unsegmented. This is the diapause stage in *Bombyx mori, Theophila mandarina* and

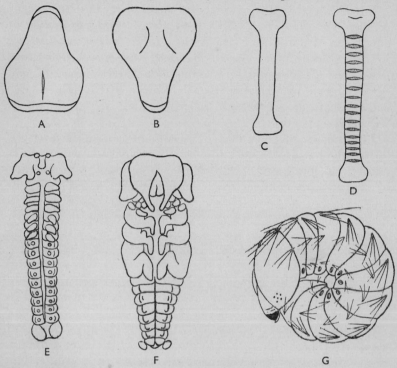

Fig. 2. Diapausing embryos of various insects (after Umeya). A, pyriform embryo—some Lepidoptera. B, reversed pyriform embryo—some Orthoptera. C, dumbbell-shaped embryo—*Bombyx mori*. D, segmented embryo—*Rhopobata naevana* (Lepidoptera). E, embryo with appendages—some Lepidoptera. F, ditto —*Locusta migratoria* and other Orthoptera. G, prelarval embryo—*Lymantria dispar* and other Lepidoptera.

other Lepidoptera and in the cricket *Gryllus mitratus* (fig. 2 C) (Umeya, 1950). In the eucosmid moth *Rhopobata naevana* the growth arrest seems to come slightly later as the somites are forming (fig. 2 D).

In many species morphogenesis is suspended at the close of anatrepsis when the somites and other axial structures are present and the embryo is apparently about to undergo revolution. The eggs of several Orthoptera (*Gryllulus commodus, Melanoplus differentialis, Locusta migratoria*) and those of the lymantriid *Orgyia antiqua* are examples (fig. 2 E, F) (Browning, 1952*a*; Slifer, 1932; Le Berre, 1953; Christensen, 1937).

Finally, development may also be halted very late in embryogenesis when the larva is fully formed and seemingly ready to hatch (fig. 2 G). This is the stage of the arrest in *Antheraea yamamai* (Saturniidae), *Lymantria dispar, Malacosoma testacea* and *M. disstria* (Lasiocampidae), also in certain Orthoptera (*Campsocleis buergeri, Melanoplus bivittatus*) (Umeya, 1950; Salt, 1949*a*) and Coleoptera (*Timarcha tenebricosa* and *T. violacea-nigra*) (Abeloos, 1935, 1941).

This survey suggests that development cannot be arrested during the phase of intense mitotic activity which accompanies blastoderm formation or during the later phase of active differentiation; these seem to be processes which, once begun, must proceed to completion. On the other hand, different species have evolved mechanisms for halting development at almost all stages during the early growth of the embryo when some cell multiplication is taking place but no cellular differentiation.

The extent of the growth arrest in the egg is often virtually complete, even at high temperatures. The rarity of mitoses in the diapause embryos of *Melanoplus differentialis* contrasts with the veritable mitotic 'explosion' which follows the resumption of growth (Slifer, 1931). But in some eggs which enter diapause at an early stage of embryogenesis the arrest is not absolute. The egg of *Austroicetes*, when exposed to moderate temperatures, will continue to develop slowly, eventually reaching the end of anatrepsis in about two months (Andrewartha, 1943). Embryogenesis in *Dociostaurus maroccanus* follows a similar course. In Iraq the egg pods of the Moroccan locust are deposited in the soil in May. The egg enters diapause within a few days when the embryo consists of a small triangular cap of cells. Slow and irregular growth takes place during the hot summer months, from 2 to 5 months being required for the completion of anatrepsis. After wintering at this stage the eggs eventually become free of diapause in the spring; the embryos then revolve round the posterior pole of the egg, active growth is resumed, and hatching finally takes place in March (Bodenheimer and Shulov, 1951). The eggs of the Lepidoptera *Notolophus thyellina* and *Dendrolimus undans* mentioned by Umeya (1950) evidently belong to the same category. In all these species there is of course only one *period* of diapause, although this condition affects several different stages of embryogenesis.

CHAPTER 2

THE ENVIRONMENT AND THE
ONSET OF DIAPAUSE

THE arrest of growth in arthropods with a facultative diapause is ultimately governed by the environment. The capacity for diapause may be realized in any generation or may remain latent indefinitely, according to the external conditions. Illustrations of this principle are numerous. By careful attention to the details of culture Cousin (1932) was able to rear the blowfly *Lucilia sericata* for eighty generations without diapause. *Pieris brassicae* has been bred continuously for 3 years at a temperature of 20–25° C. and with a photoperiod of 16 hours; after the completion of some thirty non-diapause generations there was no evidence of any loss of vigour or fertility (David and Gardiner, 1952, and personal communication). The red spider mite *Metatetranychus ulmi*, when grown under similar conditions, has yielded over seventy successive generations of females laying non-diapause summer eggs on the leaves of the host plant. On the other hand, by changing the environment the appearance of the winter females laying diapause eggs on the shoots could be evoked as readily in the first post-diapause generation as in the fiftieth (Lees, 1953 *a*). There is therefore no indication that the tendency for diapause in these species is enhanced by the failure of previous generations to experience this condition.

The nymphalid *Araschnia levana* may provide an exception to this rule. In this dimorphic species the regular alternation of diapause and non-diapause generations seems to be only partly controlled by the environment. In his experiments with *Araschnia* Süffert (1924) showed that the differing wing patterns of the spring (*levana*) and summer (*prorsa*) generations of butterflies could be attributed in part to the action of low temperature during a limited period of pupal development. A considerable

12

degree of modification in the *levana* direction was secured if the non-diapause pupae of the summer generation were chilled. But the development of the *levana* pattern seemed to be bound to the diapause condition of the overwintering generation of pupae, for these never yielded insects with *prorsa* wing patterns when incubated at high temperature. Danilyevsky (1948) has since observed that if the autumn generation of larvae are exposed from the 4th instar either to a short day length of 9 hours or to a longer one of 16 hours, all the pupae enter diapause as they would do in nature. However, *Araschia* is responsive to light, for in uninterrupted illumination the incidence of diapause falls to 13%; and all the butterflies are again of the *prorsa* type. Nevertheless, development under these circumstances is not entirely normal, the pre-emergence mortality being particularly heavy. The absence of a clear-cut response to photoperiod suggests that in this species the alternation of the two forms has acquired a degree of stability which is perhaps dependent on some internal factor.

The onset of diapause has sometimes been regarded as a direct response to unfavourable conditions. For example, Cousin (1932) considered that any departure from the optimum culture conditions—food which is unduly moist or dry, temperatures and humidities which are too high or too low—would lead to an arrest of growth in *Lucilia*. This impression may have been gained from the erratic diapause behaviour of this species. It is certainly not typical, for in most insects the various significant agencies often bear little or no relation to the immediate well-being of the individual experiencing them; rather should they be regarded as 'token' stimuli which serve to synchronize the life cycle with the seasons. The nature of these agencies and their mode of action will be considered in the following pages. Discussion of their phenological significance will be deferred until Chapter 9.

THE INFLUENCE OF PHOTOPERIOD ON THE ONSET OF DIAPAUSE

It will be shown later that diapause may be tied to a number of factors such as temperature, and the quality or quantity of the food ingested. However, these agencies must be regarded as somewhat imperfect indicators of season, for they are intrinsically variable and their influence on the insect is more or less immediate. On the other hand, the length of day possesses all the necessary attributes. It is invariable, and the response can be so adapted that the insect can enter the resistant diapause stage before the advent of unfavourable seasonal conditions. The credit for recognizing the significance of day length in controlling insect diapause belongs to Kogure, who in 1933 published a remarkably complete account of photoperiodism in the silkworm *Bombyx mori*.

The action of day length in many insects is closely linked with that of temperature. Often the maximum differential effect of typical 'long' and 'short' days is only revealed within a comparatively narrow thermal range. It will be convenient in the present context to consider photoperiod in isolation by examining the response only at these temperatures.

The relationship between photoperiod and the incidence of diapause in four insects is shown in fig. 3. The behaviour of the noctuid moth *Acronycta rumicis* when reared at 27–28° C. is typical of a large class of species (fig. 3A). If *Acronycta* is exposed during the larval feeding period to a short day length—this may range from about 6 to 15 hours—virtually every individual enters diapause in the pupal stage. As the daily photoperiod is extended to 17 hours, the incidence of diapause falls abruptly to zero; and development remains uninterrupted in continuous illumination. But some pupae also develop without arrest if the lighted hours fall below about 6 per diem; and this trend is most marked in complete darkness when only about 20 % of the insects form diapause pupae (Danilyevsky, 1948).

The general pattern of photoperiodism is very similar in several other arthropods. The photoperiodic reactions of the oriental fruit moth *Grapholitha molesta* at a temperature of 24° C. (Dickson, 1949) and those of the Tussor silkmoth *Antheraea pernyi* at 22° C. (Tanaka, 1950*b, c*) are indicated in fig. 3B and C. Very similar curves have been secured when the agrotid moth *Diataraxia oleracea* is reared at 24° C. (Way and Hopkins, 1950), and the mite *Metatetranychus ulmi* at 15° C. (Lees, 1953*a*). In all these species short or medium day lengths induce, and long day lengths prevent, diapause.

14

Bombyx, however, is exceptional in that the direction of the response is reversed (fig. 3D). When eggs and larvae of the bivoltine or quadrivoltine races are incubated at 15° C. either in darkness or in a short day of 12 hours of light, the resulting

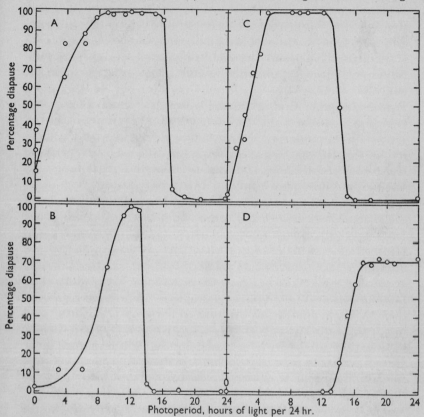

Fig. 3. The effect of photoperiod on the incidence of diapause in four species of Lepidoptera. A, *Acronycta rumicis* at 27–28° C. (after Danilyevsky). B, *Grapholitha molesta* at 24° C. (after Dickson). C, *Antheraea pernyi* (after Tanaka). D, *Bombyx mori* (bivoltine race Shohaku) at 15° C. (after Kogure).

moths lay pale eggs which develop without arrest. And with a long day length of 17 hours about 70 % of the moths lay diapause egg batches (Kogure, 1933). Eggs of the latter type are distinguishable at a glance, for during incubation the serosa becomes laden with dark pigment. Usually one individual will lay batches containing eggs of only one kind, but mixed batches are occasionally produced when the conditions are 'intermediate'.

By analogy with the terminology of the plant physiologist, *Acronycta* could be described as a 'long-day' insect. *Bombyx* is the only well-authenticated example of a 'short-day' species, although some stocks of *Antheraea pernyi* and *Dasychira pudibunda* (Orgyidae) have been reported as responding in similar fashion (Gayspitz, 1953). Many other insects are doubtless 'day-length neutral'. Among these insensitive species are the Lepidoptera *Phalera bucephala* and *Spilosoma menthastri* (Danilyevsky and Gayspitz, 1948) and the weevil *Listroderes* (Dickson, 1949).

Certain Lepidoptera which hibernate as larvae display a modified form of 'long-day' response. For example, *Dendrolimus pini* (Lasiocampidae) differs fundamentally from the species described above in that the arrest of growth remains under the imminent control of day length throughout the period of dormancy. Larvae of any instar can be induced to enter diapause by exposure to a short day of 9 hours; but growth is again resumed after a delay of 2 weeks if the diapausing larvae are illuminated continuously or are kept in the dark (Danilyevsky, 1948; Gayspitz, 1949). *Euproctis similis, E. chrysorrhoea* and *Leucoma salicis* (Orgyidae) also react to photoperiod, despite their strictly univoltine rhythm in nature. Growth and moulting of the larvae is greatly retarded with all photoperiods shorter than about 17 hours, and, indeed, in permanent light also (Gayspitz, 1953). But within a narrow intermediate range (*c.* 17–22 hours) a proportion of the larvae (reaching 100 % in the case of *Euproctis similis*, 64 % in *E. chrysorrhoea* and 53 % in *Leucoma*) develop without delay; and those larvae which still enter diapause with an optimal photoperiod of 20 hours tend to do so in a later instar. Although the light factor operates during the post-hibernation period as well as during pre-hibernation, it is not entirely clear whether these three species also retain their sensitivity to photoperiod when completely dormant, or whether an additional agency, such as low temperature, is concerned in the disappearance of diapause.

Attention may be called also to certain lesser differences in the response to day length. One significant variant is the duration

16

of the 'intermediate' or 'critical' photoperiod. In stocks of *Acronycta* collected in the Leningrad region the rate of change in the incidence of diapause becomes most rapid when the day length has fallen to about 16 hours. In *Diataraxia* day length becomes transitional at about 15 hours, in *Antheraea* and *Metatetranychus* at 14–15 hours and in Californian populations of *Grapholitha* at 13–14 hours (fig. 3). No doubt these differences represent adjustments to the seasonal fluctuation of day length within the area of distribution. Species from low latitudes where the differential between the summer solstice and the equinox is relatively narrow must be expected to respond to shorter critical photoperiods, otherwise diapause would not be averted during the favourable season.

A second feature illustrated in fig. 3 is the partial absence of diapause in very short photoperiods or in darkness. This trend usually becomes apparent as the photoperiod falls below the shortest day length that would be encountered in nature. Under these conditions a proportion of the insects experiencing very short photoperiods are no doubt reacting to complete darkness. The response to the absence of light varies according to species. *Pieris brassicae* forms no diapause pupae at all (Danilyevsky and Gayspitz, 1948); in *Grapholitha* and in *Antheraea* diapause is confined to about 2 % of the larvae and pupae respectively. In *Acronycta* the incidence of diapause may vary between 20 and 37 % in different experiments; in *Metatetranychus* about 60 % of the female mites reared in darkness lay winter eggs. In *Diataraxia* about 80 % of the pupae enter diapause. Finally, *Bombyx* responds no differently than to a short day of 8 hours.

Many other arthropods are known to be sensitive to the length of day. The following instances may all be placed in the 'long-day' category. Thus diapause is averted by long photoperiods in the codling moth *Cydia pomonella* (Dickson, 1949), in the eucosmid *Polychrosis botrana* (Komarova, 1949) and in the zygaenid *Harrisina brillians* (Smith and Langston, 1953). Long photoperiods also favour continuous reproduction in *Tetranychus telarius*, whereas exposure to short photoperiods soon causes the female mites to cease feeding and gradually to assume the striking scarlet pigmentation of the hibernating form (Lees, 1953a). It is also known that continuous illumination will prevent cyclical hibernation in the English anautogenous race of *Culex pipiens pipiens* (Tate and Vincent, 1936). And a similar treatment facilitates the growth and reproduction of the grouse locust *Acrydium arenosum* during the winter months (Sabrosky, Larsen and Nabours, 1933).

Photoperiod is also a significant factor in the inception of diapause in the Colorado beetle *Leptinotarsa*, although its role is perhaps less decisive than in some of the species mentioned above. Diapause sets in soon after the imaginal moult if the insects have been exposed to a 10-hour photoperiod at temperatures of 21–28° C. As the feeding activity subsides, the beetles gradually acquire a strong positive geotaxis and lose the positive phototaxis that is displayed during the pre-diapause feeding period. They finally enter the soil without ovipositing. Diapause is not completely prevented by a 15-hour photoperiod, although some individuals lay a few eggs before becoming dormant. However, at least three-quarters of the beetles reared at 28° C. remain in full breeding condition if the photoperiod is extended to 20 hours (de Wilde, 1953, and personal communication).

THE RESPONSE TO CONSTANT AND CHANGING PHOTOPERIODS

Unlike many vertebrates, the majority of arthropods probably respond to the actual duration of the light and dark components of the cycle of illumination and not to the change in day length. For example, although in nature the winter females of *Metatetranychus* appear in late summer as the days are shortening, only summer females are differentiated if the developing mites are subjected to a long photoperiod falling each day by 7 minutes (Lees, 1953 a). Similarly, diapause is not prevented in *Grapholitha* if the illumination is extended by a regular daily increment of 5 minutes, provided the insects experience a short day length during the sensitive period of larval development (Dickson, 1949). These results are hardly surprising in view of the high intrinsic rate of development in these species and the short time span, often only a few days, during which each individual is sensitive to this stimulus (see p. 32).

The Environment and the Onset of Diapause

Recent studies by Corbet (1954) suggest, nevertheless, that in a more slowly developing insect, namely, the dragonfly *Anax imperator*, the onset of diapause is influenced by the progression of the photoperiod. Under English conditions any nymph entering the final (diapause) instar after the end of June fails to undergo metamorphosis until the following spring. Nymphs in their penultimate instar, together with those which had just entered the final instar, were collected in the field in July and exposed to different day-length régimes. The insects experiencing a constant long photoperiod of $15\frac{1}{2}$ hours at a mean temperature of $24°$ C. entered a diapause which lasted over 100 days. The arrest of growth was equally prolonged if the nymphs experienced an initial photoperiod of 16 hours, falling by 3 minutes daily to 8 hours in December. But many insects metamorphosed promptly within 30 days if the initial 16-hour photoperiod was extended by 3 minutes daily. It seems that successive small increments and single large increases are both effective.

THE SENSITIVITY TO ILLUMINATION; SPECTRAL SENSITIVITY

It has proved a general rule that the photoperiodic reaction in arthropods is independent of intensity and total light energy provided the intensity exceeds a certain limiting value. The threshold of perception of white light is usually in the region of 1 foot-candle; dimmer illumination is then equivalent to darkness. In the silkworm egg the threshold of sensitivity at $15°$ C. is no higher than 0.01 f.c. and in the larva 0.08 f.c. (Kogure, 1933). The larvae of *Grapholitha* will respond to a photoperiod if the light intensity reaching the surface of the immature apples in which they are tunnelling exceeds $1–3$ f.c. Although Dickson (1949) points out that these fruits are appreciably translucent, the actual sensitivity of the larvae must of course be considerably greater. In two other lepidopterous insects, *Diataraxia* and *Acronycta*, the threshold is known to be below 1 and 0.5 f.c. respectively (Way and Hopkins, 1950; Danilyevsky, 1948). And in *Metatetranychus* the threshold is $1–2$ f.c. (Lees, 1953a). These values, though striking, do not compare with the performance of some photoreceptors, among which the human eye with a limiting sensitivity of the order of 10^{-7} f.c. is the most impressive.

Two further points are worthy of note. As a device for measuring time, it is clearly necessary that the photoperiodic reaction should be independent of random diurnal fluctuations in light intensity. And some significance may perhaps be attached to the fact that the threshold of sensitivity seems to lie just above the intensity of direct moonlight which usually falls within the range 0·01–0·05 f.c.

Although accurate action spectra are not yet available, experiments employing filtered light have shown that wavelengths in the blue and blue-green regions of the spectrum are the most active photoperiodically. The following results were obtained in *Bombyx* by Kogure (1933). When eggs of the bivoltine race *Showa* were irradiated continuously with violet light of wavelength 350–510 mμ at an incubation temperature of 15° C., 98 % of the resulting moths laid batches of dark eggs; the incidence of diapause was only 8 % with orange-yellow light of approximately the same relative energy; and with red light only 3% laid diapause egg batches, a figure no higher than in the controls which were incubated in the dark. *Grapholitha* is totally insensitive to infra-red and ultra-violet radiation (Dickson, 1949). A slight response was obtained with a deep red filter transmitting wavelengths above 600 mμ. But the maximum sensitivity was recorded with blue-green and green-yellow light. In comparison with this species, the effective waveband in *Metatetranychus* is displaced slightly towards the ultra-violet. Maximum sensitivity lies in the blue region of the spectrum at a wavelength of *c.* 425 mμ but extends on either side into the near-ultra-violet (*c.* 365 mμ) and blue-green (*c.* 500 mμ). The mites proved to be entirely insensitive to wavelengths longer than 530 mμ (i.e. to yellow, red or infra-red radiation), even if the relative energy of the incident beam was over one thousand times greater than that required to produce a threshold response with blue light (Lees, 1953*a*).

The identity of the photodynamic agent is not known. Parker, Hendricks, Borthwick and Jenner (1952) have recently suggested that there is a general uniformity in the action spectra of photoperiodically controlled processes in plants (e.g.

flowering, promotion of leaf elongation, etc.) and animals (diapause, reproductive cycles of birds and mammals, etc.). If this were established, the similarity might be expected to extend in some measure to the light-sensitive pigment. It is now clear, however, that the spectral sensitivity of the reaction controlling diapause is quite unlike that in plants, for in the latter effectiveness is invariably greatest in the red wavelengths (620–660 mμ). The open-chain tetrapyrrolic pigments of the type suggested for plants would not have the required absorption characteristics. Cyclic tetrapyrroles (e.g. the ferroprotoporphyrins), which have an absorption maximum in the blue as well as other maxima at wavelengths above 500 mμ, are possible candidates. However, unless there is a strong screening effect from other pigments (which the low threshold of intensity does not suggest), it is difficult on this basis to account for the total loss of sensitivity to wavelengths in the yellow-red region. Perhaps carotenoids are concerned in photoreception.

THE SITE OF PHOTORECEPTION

As many of the arthropods which exhibit photoperiodism are phytophagous, it has been necessary to consider whether diapause in these species may not be influenced indirectly by photoperiodic reactions set up in the plant. Way and Hopkins (1950) reared *Diataraxia* in a diapause-preventing photoperiod of 16 hours but fed the larvae on cabbage plants grown in a 12-hour photoperiod. The pupae obtained were all of the non-diapause type, thereby proving that the plant was not concerned in the mediation of the response. Experiments with *Metatetranychus* have yielded a similar result; and the further possibility that diapause in this species is affected by differences in the feeding activity during light and darkness has also been excluded (Lees, 1953*a*).

This evidence suggests that the insect or mite is influenced directly by the cycle of illumination. One might anticipate that the eyes would prove to be the photoreceptors, but Tanaka (1950*c*) has demonstrated that this is not the case in *Antheraea*. This species is a particularly suitable subject, since the arrest of growth is completely prevented in darkness. If the insects are exposed to a short-day régime, the elimination of the photo-receptive mechanism will then be revealed by the total absence of diapause. Larvae in which the lateral ocelli were covered with enamel during the whole of the larval period, and those in which the ocelli were destroyed in the 4th instar with a cautery, all formed diapause pupae in response to a short day length.

It remains to be decided whether the photoreceptive area is situated in the epidermis, or whether, as seems more probable, light penetrates the integument and affects some internal organ such as the central nervous system.

THE MODE OF ACTION OF THE CYCLE OF ILLUMINATION

Plant physiologists have emphasized that the term 'photo-periodism' is something of a misnomer, since it is now well established that the intervening dark phase plays at least as significant a role as the photoperiod in suppressing or inducing the formation of flower primordia (Borthwick, Parker and Hendricks, 1950). The same conclusion can be drawn from recent researches of the control of diapause by day length.

The comprehensive experiments of Dickson (1949) have shown that the absolute duration of both the light and the dark phases of the cycle of illumination are involved in the determination of diapause in *Grapholitha*. The conditions which induce diapause are extremely narrow. The duration of the light phase must fall between 7 and 15 hours and that of the dark phase between 11 and 16 hours. All cycles in which the duration of either component is longer or shorter than these values causes the larvae to pupate without diapause. The mechanism of control is here linked closely with the natural 24-hour cycle of light and darkness.

The induction of diapause also requires rather special conditions in *Acronycta*, namely, a dark phase of critical duration (Danilyevsky and Glinyanaya, 1949, 1950). Fig. 4 has been constructed from the results obtained by these writers. It will be noted that the arrest is always prevented when the dark phase is shorter than 9 hours or longer than 24 hours. Cycles including dark phases of 6 (C), 48 (F), 72 (G) or 216 hours all permit uninterrupted development. The type of experiment shown in fig. 4D–G, in which the cycle is divided equally into periods of

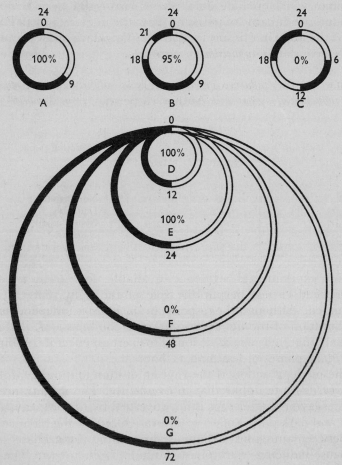

Fig. 4. The influence of different cycles of illumination on the induction of diapause in *Acronycta rumicis* (after Danilyevsky). The duration of the cycle or half-cycle in hours is indicated outside each ring; the percentage of pupae entering diapause is shown inside.

light and darkness, also demonstrates clearly that the *ratio* of the light and dark hours is of no intrinsic significance.

The dark phase is also of primary importance in *Antheraea*. If it exceeds 11 hours, all the pupae enter diapause apparently without regard to the duration of the light period (Tanaka, 1950*c*, 1951*a*). The salient features are summarized in table 1. Régimes which include dark phases lasting for periods up to 39 hours are capable of inducing diapause in every pupa. There is no indication in this species that very long dark phases become ineffective as in *Grapholitha* or *Acronycta*.

TABLE 1. *The influence of different cycles of illumination on the induction of diapause in* Antheraea pernyi (*from Tanaka*)

Cycle (hr.)	Duration of light and dark periods (hr.)		Condition of pupae
	Light	Dark	
24	< 13	> 11	Diapause
	> 15	< 9	Non-diapause
48	< 37	> 11	Diapause
	> 39	< 9	Non-diapause
72	< 59	> 13	Diapause
	> 62	< 10	Non-diapause

The experimental evidence available for *Acronycta* and *Antheraea* does not permit the role of the light phase to be evaluated. Although the response in *Antheraea* is independent of the duration of the light phase in some combinations, it is not unlikely that light would be found to exert an effect if combined with dark phases of less than 11 hours.

The mode of action of the rhythm of illumination in *Metatetranychus* is quite unlike that in *Grapholitha*. The appearance of females laying winter eggs is not governed by the occurrence of light and dark phases of critical duration but by the balance set up between antagonistic diapause-preventing (light phase) and diapause-inducing (dark phase) stimuli (Lees, 1953*b*). The influence of the light phase can be seen clearly when the period of darkness is of short duration, say 4 or 8 hours. Then the effectiveness of the photoperiod increases progressively as the duration is extended from 8 to 16 hours (fig. 5). The effectiveness of the dark phase in promoting diapause also rises with duration, but the rate of increase with successive increments is strikingly non-linear. For example, an 8-hour dark period is completely overcome by a 16-hour photoperiod, but 12 hours of darkness, as in

Antheraea, can annul photoperiods as long as 36 hours. No further increase in activity appears to occur with a further extension of the dark period to 24 hours.

It will be apparent that although both light- and dark-phase reactions become more influential with time, they do so at different rates and apparently attain a different peak effectiveness. The mode of action of different régimes in *Metatetranychus*

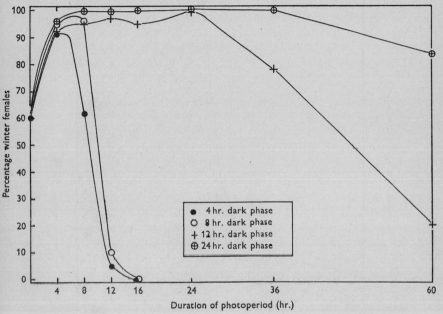

Fig. 5. The influence of the cycle of illumination on the induction of diapause in the mite *Metatetranychus ulmi* (after Lees). Note that the potency of the dark phase in inducing diapause is rapidly augmented as it is extended from 8 to 12 hours.

therefore depends to a great extent on the absolute length of both the light and dark phases. Owing to the overriding influence of a long dark period, and also to the balanced reactions which are observed with shorter phases, the conditions which can evoke diapause in *Metatetranychus* are far more varied than in *Grapholitha*. This contrast is brought out in fig. 6.

The flowering of many plants is controlled principally by the duration of the dark period; the light-phase reaction proceeds to completion so rapidly that it is virtually independent of time.

Physiology of Diapause in Arthropods

It follows that the flowering of short-day plants is readily suppressed, and that of long-day plants initiated, if the long dark

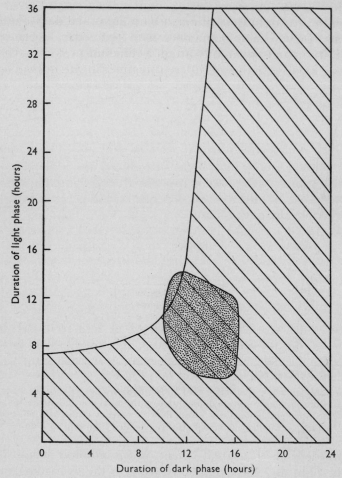

Fig. 6. Chart showing the combinations of light and darkness which produce more than 50% of diapausing individuals. Stippled area: *Grapholitha molesta* at 24° C. (after Dickson). Shaded area: *Metatetranychus ulmi* at 15° C. (after Lees).

phase in a short-day cycle is broken by quite brief lighted intervals of 30 minutes or less.

The photoperiodic mechanism in arthropods such as *Grapholitha* and *Metatetranychus* differs fundamentally from this pattern

26

for, as we have seen, slow timing reactions take place during both the dark and the light periods. These species, and probably many other arthropods as well, are therefore relatively insensitive to short interpolated intervals of light. In *Grapholitha* a long dark phase (D) must be interrupted for 2 hours (L) before the incidence of diapause is reduced by one-half:

Cycle	Régime	% diapause
24 hr.	12 L, 12 D	99
	11 L, 6 D, 1 L, 6 D	81
	10 L, 6 D, 2 L, 6 D	55

In *Acronycta* a 3-hour light break introduced into a diapause-inducing 15-hour dark phase is capable of abolishing diapause completely, but its effectiveness depends on the point of introduction within the dark phase:

Cycle	Régime	% diapause
24 hr.	9 L, 15 D	100
	9 L, 6 D, 3 L, 6 D	7
	9 L, 9 D, 3 L, 3 D	95

Since an uninterrupted dark period of at least 9 hours is essential for the induction of diapause, this condition is prevented most strongly when the dark phase is divided into two equal periods of 6 hours (see also fig. 4 A–C).

In *Metatetranychus* the effect of a 6-hour interruption is perceptible, but not one of 2 or 4 hours:

Cycle	Régime	% winter females
24 hr.	8 L, 16 D	100
	8 L, 6 D, 4 L, 6 D	100
	8 L, 5 D, 6 L, 5 D	76

These arthropods have proved to be equally insensitive to the inclusion of short dark intervals within a photoperiod of critical length. For example, the inducing reaction in *Grapholitha* is only considerably disturbed when a short diapause-inducing

27

photoperiod of 12 hours is 'split' by dark periods of 2 or 3 hours:

Cycle	Régime	% diapause
24 hr.	12L, 12D	98
24 hr.	6L, 1D, 6L, 11D	93
25 hr.	6L, 2D, 6L, 11D	62
26 hr.	6L, 3D, 6L, 11D	3

In addition to the phase length, the *number* of light and dark periods which are experienced during development may also be crucial. *Metatetranychus* requires about 8 days at 15° C. to develop from the deutonymph to the adult stage, and it is during this period that the mites are most sensitive to the rhythm of illumination. Deutonymphs which are exposed throughout this period to a 24-hour cycle equally divided into light and dark phases will of course develop as winter females. By introducing one or more diapause-preventing long-day cycles into this régime it is possible to show that development is only completely 'switched over' in favour of the diapause condition when the mites experience seven or eight short dark phases of 12 hours. If the dark phase is maintained at 12 hours, and the photoperiod extended until the total cycle occupies 48 or 72 hours, the number of dark phases which fall within the sensitive period will decrease to 4 and 2–3 respectively. It is probable that the decline in the incidence of winter females which is observed when photoperiods of 36 and 60 hours are employed (see fig. 5), may be connected with this circumstance rather than with the ability of very long photoperiods to overcome a 12-hour dark phase.

It would be premature to attempt any detailed interpretation of these results in physiological terms. Nevertheless, in such species as *Antheraea* and *Metatetranychus*, the type of interaction observed does suggest that some active product capable either of preventing or inducing diapause is synthesized during one phase and is then destroyed or removed from the sphere of action during the succeeding phase. From their slow inception it is evident that the dark- and light-phase reactions either increase in velocity with time or build up to a threshold. There must also be some means of transferring the active product to the next cycle, since the effect of consecutive cycles is cumulative. However, in the case of *Grapholitha* it is almost impossible to apply a simple hypothesis of this kind, for the direction in which the light or dark phase acts is apparently reversed twice as the duration of the phase is extended successively: a short phase will prevent diapause, a rather longer phase of critical duration will induce diapause, and a still longer phase will again prevent diapause.

Similar difficulties arise in connexion with the absence of diapause which, as we have noted, is of frequent occurrence when the insect is reared continuously in the absence of light. Danilyevsky and Glinyanaya (1950) compare the action of continuous darkness with that of continuous illumination, and suggest that the mechanism of arrest cannot function when a rhythmical alteration of light and darkness is lacking. But the physiological explanation is unknown.

TEMPERATURE AND THE ONSET OF DIAPAUSE

In the Lepidoptera *Antheraea* and *Harrisina*, photoperiod has assumed so dominant a role that the arrest of growth is virtually independent of temperature (Tanaka, 1944; Smith and Langston, 1953). However, this is by no means typical, for in most arthropods temperature plays an influential part in controlling the onset of diapause.

As a rule, high temperatures tend to avert diapause while low temperatures favour the arrest of growth. This type of response is shown by *Diataraxia* and *Metatetranychus* (fig. 7A, B). It will be noted that when *Diataraxia* is reared at 34° C., all the pupae develop without arrest if the larvae have also experienced a long day length, and that diapause is prevented in about half the pupae which have been exposed to short day lengths. Conversely, at low temperatures of 12 and 15° C. over 90 % of the pupae enter diapause even though the larvae have experienced a long photoperiod (Way and Hopkins, 1950). In this way the effect of the day length is partially or completely masked except within the medium temperature range. Very similar results have been obtained with *Metatetranychus* (Fig. 7B) (Lees, 1953a).

Nevertheless, this rule is by no means universal. In

29

Physiology of Diapause in Arthropods

Grapholitha both high and low temperatures prevent diapause (Fig. 7 C) (Dickson, 1949). And in *Bombyx* diapause is induced by high temperatures and averted by low temperatures (fig. 7 D)

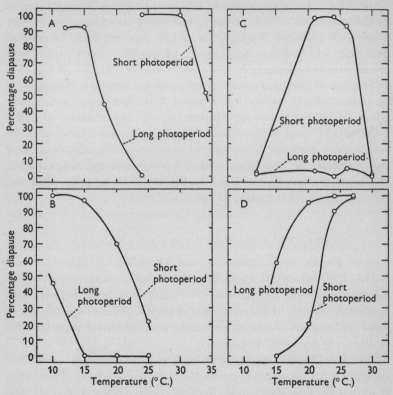

Fig. 7. The combined action of temperature and photoperiod on the induction of diapause. A, *Diataraxia oleracea* (after Way and Hopkins). B, *Metatetranychus ulmi* (after Lees). C, *Grapholitha molesta* (after Dickson). D, *Bombyx mori* race Shohaku (after Kogure). The long and short photoperiods were as follows: A, 16 and 8 hours; B, 16 and 12 hours; C, 15 and 12 hours; D, 16 and 12 hours. In all cases the total cycle lasted for 24 hours.

(Watanabe, 1918, cited in Kuwana, 1932; Kogure, 1933). High temperatures and long day lengths therefore act in concert, just as in *Diataraxia* or *Metatetranychus*, but the direction of the response is reversed.

The action of high temperature in suppressing the onset of diapause has been described in many other insects, including

The Environment and the Onset of Diapause

the Lepidoptera *Pieris brassicae* (Maercks, 1934), *Heliothis armigera* (Ditman, Weiland and Guill, 1940), *Loxostege sticticalis* (Steinberg and Kamensky, 1936), *Pyrausta nubilalis* (Kozhant-shikov, 1938*b*), *Chilo simplex* (Fukaya, 1950), *Orgyia gonostigma* (Kozhantshikov, 1948), *Telea polyphemus* (Dawson, 1931) and *Philosamia cynthia* (Danilyevsky, 1939). The sandfly *Phlebotomus papatasii* (Theodor, 1934), the mosquito *Finlaya geniculata* (Roubaud and Colas-Belcour, 1926) and the pentatomid *Eury-dema ornatum* (Bonnemaison, 1948*a, b*) are further examples.

The mode of action of temperature has been very little studied. The frequent association of low temperature with the inception of diapause has led some authors to conclude that this factor influences the processes of growth through the medium of the metabolism (e.g. Simmonds, 1948; Andrewartha, 1952). However, recent experience with species such as *Diataraxia* and *Metatetranychus* suggests rather that temperature should be regarded as a 'token' stimulus in the same sense as photoperiod. Indeed, it may well be that these two agencies react with the same physiological mechanism. Some evidence in favour of this hypothesis has been secured in *Metatetranychus*.

When developing mites are exposed to a 24-hour cycle of illumination equally divided into light and dark periods, the incidence of winter females approaches 100 % at 15° C. but is reduced to *c.* 21 % if the mites experience a constant temperature of 25° C. The following results were obtained in experiments employing fluctuating temperatures (Lees, 1953*a*):

Régime	% winter females
12 hr. L at 25° C., 12 hr. D at 15° C.	96
12 hr. L at 15° C., 12 hr. D at 25° C.	53

It will be noted that high temperature is ineffective if given con-currently with light, but is influential during the dark phase. Since the light- and dark-phase reactions may well involve entirely different processes, temperature could be visualized as influencing one but not the other. An alternative hypothesis, due to M. J. Way (personal communication), suggests the possi-bility that slow timing reactions are involved. A high-temperature thermoperiod lasting for 12 hours, followed by a short photoperiod, might approach the efficacy of a long photoperiod in preventing diapause. But a high-temperature phase coinciding with the photoperiod would not be expected to enhance the reaction if this were already maximal. Further research is needed to settle this question.

STAGES OF DEVELOPMENT SENSITIVE TO PHOTOPERIOD AND TEMPERATURE

The physical factors which control the onset of diapause often operate on the insect long before growth is finally arrested. The period when the developing insect is most responsive to these stimuli is characteristic of the species. Sometimes the period of sensitivity extends over several instars; sometimes it is localized in one particular instar. During this sensitive period the physiological mechanism which is later to control growth is 'switched' by the environment into one of two strictly alternative pathways—the diapause or the non-diapause. This can be regarded as a process of determination, since it is often found that once the insect has passed through this stage of development the environment is no longer influential. These principles are most easily illustrated by reference to factors such as photoperiod and temperature.

TABLE 2. *The effect of continuous light or darkness on the eggs and early larval instars of* Bombyx mori (*from Kogure*). *Incubation temperature, 19° C.*

Treatment of eggs and larvae	% moths laying diapause egg batches
Egg and 1st, 2nd and 3rd instars in darkness	2
Egg in darkness, 3rd instar illuminated	21
Egg in darkness, 2nd instar illuminated	38
Egg in darkness, 1st instar illuminated	41
Egg in darkness, 1st, 2nd and 3rd instars illuminated	45
Egg illuminated	97

Bombyx is remarkable in that the period of determination precedes the stage of arrest by almost an entire generation. In general, the type of egg is decided by the conditions experienced by the moth while in the egg stage, although some sensitivity to temperature and photoperiod is retained by the early larval instars (Kogure, 1933). Thus the observations summarized in table 2 show that the illumination of the first three larval instars, or of any instar separately, after dark incubation, is much less effective in inducing diapause than the illumination of the egg. A further significant feature is that the egg only becomes responsive quite late in embryogenesis when all the organ systems have been differentiated.

In other insects the stages of sensitivity and of diapause are less widely separated. In *Polychrosis botrana*, which enters diapause as a pupa, photoperiod is again most influential during embryonic growth. Komarova (1949) has reared this eucosmid in a long day length at 25–30° C., transferring some individuals at each moult to a short day of 12 hours. The following results show that there is a gradual loss of responsiveness in each successive instar:

Stage transferred	Egg	1st instar	2nd instar	3rd instar	4th instar
% diapause pupae	100	23	13	5	0

The nymphalid *Araschnia* also possesses a pupal diapause, but the period of sensitivity to light here occurs during the penultimate and last (4th and 5th) larval instars. In insects which have entered the 4th instar about 6 long-day cycles are sufficient to prevent diapause completely (Danilyevsky, 1948). The 4th and 5th are also the critical instars in *Telea polyphemus* and *Philosamia cynthia* (Dawson, 1931; Danilyevsky, 1939).

Other species may remain responsive to the environment up to the point of entry into diapause and some, of which *Dendrolimus* is an example (p. 16), retain this sensitivity throughout the period of dormancy. In *Metatetranychus* the pattern of reproduction is normally laid down during the last or deutonymphal instar. Yet the function of the ovaries remains labile even after the adult mite has begun to lay eggs. If winter females that have been reared in a short day length are exposed to a long day length at 15° C., they continue to lay diapause eggs for about 2 weeks. But after this time lapse the mites usually switch over to eggs of the summer type. This reversal, which is

33

accompanied by a change in the pattern of behaviour, is usually rapid and complete, although a few eggs of intermediate size and pigmentation are sometimes laid during the period of transition. The 'switch-over' will take place in either direction with equal facility. Nevertheless, it is apparent that the female mite is much less sensitive to day length than the deutonymph, since fourteen or more cycles are required to effect the reversal, compared with only eight in the deutonymph (Lees, 1953a).

The determination process is also partially reversible in *Leptinotarsa*. Beetles that have just entered diapause in response to a short photoperiod are restored to full reproductive activity by exposure to an antagonistic photoperiod. However, once *Leptinotarsa* is completely dormant, day length is no longer influential. Diapause must then run its course, and other stimuli, notably a suitable temperature, are required for the termination of the growth arrest (de Wilde, personal communication).

The duration of the sensitive period is another highly variable feature. In *Diataraxia* the period of greatest sensitivity occurs during the 'moulting sleep' of the penultimate instar larva and lasts for no longer than 2 days. One or two long-day cycles at this time are sufficient to prevent the diapause in 80 % of the pupae (Way and Hopkins, 1950).

On the other hand, the larvae of *Grapholitha* remain responsive to photoperiod throughout the feeding period (Dickson, 1949). Strict delimitation of the sensitive period is also lacking in *Antheraea*; all the larval stadia and perhaps even the eggs exhibit some sensitivity to light, although the later instars are probably more critical than the earlier. A selection from the long series of experiments by Tanaka (1950a, b) is shown in fig. 8. The exposure of any one instar to short day lengths hardly induces any pupae to enter diapause provided the remaining instars are grown in long photoperiods. The effect becomes progressively greater when two or three consecutive instars experience the short-day treatment. However, the slightly enhanced responsiveness of the older larvae can be detected by exposing the other instars to a critical photoperiod of 14 hours. When *Antheraea* is reared throughout with a day length of this duration, diapause and non-diapause pupae are formed in almost equal numbers. Against this 'neutral' background the effect of exposing even single stadia to long- or short-day conditions becomes readily apparent (fig. 8).

It will be observed that in all the examples noted above the sensitivity to external factors is only acquired when the central nervous and endocrine systems are already in existence; and

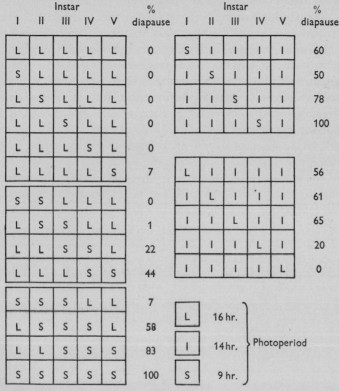

Fig. 8. The effect on the incidence of pupal diapause of exposing the different larval instars of *Antheraea pernyi* to typical long, short or 'intermediate' photoperiods (after Tanaka).

further, that the final events leading up to the onset of diapause take place within the life of the individual. The latter statement applies even to *Bombyx*, for embryonic diapause in this species is essentially a maternal character (see p. 101). It may well be, therefore, that these organ systems are concerned in the transmission of the stimulus during the interval separating the

35

sensitive period and the arrest of growth. There are, neverthe-less, a few exceptional cases in which the stimulus appears to be communicated from parent to offspring through the egg. The pteromalid *Spalangia drosophilae*, a pupal ectoparasite of the fritfly, is one example (Simmonds, 1948). Much of the diapause which affects the 3rd-instar larvae is eliminated if the parasites are bred throughout at high temperatures (table 3A). But the suppressive effect of this factor is still more pronounced when the parental generation is reared at a lower temperature than the ovipositing females and progeny (table 3B). Simmonds attributes this result to metabolic stimulation; and he considers that the changed pattern of metabolism, after transmission through the egg, ultimately influences the growth of the larva in its last instar.

TABLE 3. *The effect of temperature on the induction of diapause in* Spalangia drosophilae *(from Simmonds)*

Temperature, in ° C., during development of		% progeny entering diapause
Parent generation	Progeny	
A 28	28	31
24	24	88
21	21	*
B 21	28	3
21	24	9
24	28	6

* All the parent generation entered diapause.

There is also some evidence that diapause in the 3rd-instar larva of *Lucilia* is of maternal origin. Cragg and Cole (1952) collected flies in the field at different seasons and reared their progeny at a temperature (26° C.) that prevented diapause in over 90 % of the controls. The eggs laid during the first 24 hours after capture yielded less than 20 % of diapausing larvae in July, but this figure increased progressively to 96 % in October, sug-gesting that some general physical factor had already operated on the maternal generation.

The Environment and the Onset of Diapause

THE EFFECT OF DIET ON THE ONSET
OF DIAPAUSE

The food of many phytophagous insects changes with such regularity through the year that it would be surprising if this factor did not sometimes serve as an index of season. Yet despite the frequent observation that the onset of diapause coincides with some distinctive phase in the growth cycle of the host plant, experiment has often revealed that there is no causal connexion between these events. The feeding habits of the trivoltine moth *Polychrosis botrana* may be taken as an example. In the Ukraine the first-generation larvae feed regularly on the inflorescences of the vine, the second on unripe berries and the third on mature berries with a high sugar content. Nevertheless, the diet appropriate to the second- and third-generation larvae can be interchanged without in any way affecting the incidence of diapause in these generations (Komarova, 1949).

Diapause sometimes appears to be induced by starvation. The partially grown larvae of the subtropical borer *Diatraea lineolata* (Crambidae) often become dormant when tunnelling in dry maize stalks (Kevan, 1944). In this instance diapause is associated with the poor food value of the plant, and not with its moisture content, for dormancy can be induced by transferring larvae from green cornstalks to dead material which is kept moistened. A failure of the food supplies will also lead to the onset of diapause in *Metatetranychus* (Lees, 1953a). If the mites are fed either on tender young apple foliage or on fully mature, deep green leaves, the diet exercises no influence at all; the incidence of winter and summer females is then decided only by the photoperiod and temperature. But if the developing mites are fed on senescing leaves showing patches of yellow, winter females appear in large numbers even when photoperiod and temperature are such as to prevent diapause strongly. The same result is also observed when the leaves of the host plant are heavily damaged by the feeding punctures of previous mite populations—a condition known as bronzing. A feature common to both the bronzed and the senescent leaf is the great reduction in the numbers of intact palisade and mesophyll cells, upon the contents of which the mite feeds. Long-continued under-nourishment extending over the sensitive period may well be the causal agency.

The falling water content of the maturing plant has often been suspected of evoking diapause, but well-attested instances are rare. The relative content of water and fat in the cotton boll has been regarded as the significant agency in the pink boll-worm *Platyedra gossypiella* (Squire, 1939, 1940; Fife, 1949). Ecological observations by Squire in the West Indies have shown that there is an apparent relationship with boll develop-ment. Only 5 % of the larvae feeding on green bolls with a moisture content of 70–80 % were found to be dormant, whereas ripe bolls containing much fat and less than 20 % of water yielded 62 %. However, as *Platyedra* has not yet been reared under controlled conditions, it is impossible to decide whether these factors are indeed causal, as these authors contend. Working with *Loxostege sticticalis*, Strelnikov (1936) concluded that the onset of diapause was associated with the low water content of the food plant. On the other hand, Steinberg and Kamensky (1936) believed that diapause in this species was connected with some qualitative change in the diet. Neither view was confirmed by Pepper and Hastings (1941), who could detect no influence on diapause when larvae were reared at controlled temperatures on *Artemisia* with a water content of 69 % and on sugar beet containing 86 % of water. This con-fusion may well have arisen because some essential component of the environment, probably day length, has been overlooked. Rapid growth in *Euproctis phaeorrhoea* (= *E. chrysorrhoea*), and the ensuing failure of the larvae to enter diapause in the 2nd or 3rd instar, was considered by Grison (1947) to be favoured by a diet consisting of young foliage. However, Gayspitz (1953) could trace no association between leaf age and diapause either in *E. chrysorrhoea* or *E. similis*, although nutrition appeared to have a slight effect upon *Leucoma salicis*. In the case of these orgyid moths, the dominant factor is now known to be the length of day (p. 16).

The growth of certain hymenopterous parasites is undoubtedly governed by the quality of the food. In the eulophid *Melittobia chalybii*, a gregarious external parasite of the wasp *Trypoxylon*, the rate of larval development, and the form of the imago, is determined by the parts of the dead host which are available as food for the larvae. The first sixteen or so parasite larvae to hatch ingest all the blood of the fresh host and proceed to develop in about 14 days into brachypterous adults. The remaining larvae, often numbering several hundred, consume the tissues of the host. All the latter develop slowly in about 90 days into macropterous individuals (Schmieder, 1933).

THE INFLUENCE OF AGE AND OTHER MATERNAL CHARACTERS

The close link which exists between the inception of diapause and the external environment will hardly need further stressing. However, there remain a small number of instances in which a connexion has been traced between diapause and some physiological character, such as maternal age, which bears no direct relation to the environment.

Although the results are curiously irregular, the probability that the larvae of *Spalangia* will enter diapause is apparently increased if they have hatched from eggs laid by senile females (Simmonds, 1948). According to Roubaud (1928), the larvae of *Phlebotomus* will develop without arrest if they have hatched from eggs laid within 5 days of the blood meal, whereas the tendency is for the later larvae to enter diapause. It is said that eggs laid during the initial period will furnish diapausing 4th-instar larvae if oviposition is artificially retarded by denying the midges soil on which to lay. This is attributed to a hypothetical inhibitory principle which is passed to the larvae from the overripe eggs.

The proportion of diapause and non-diapause eggs in the egg pods of *Locustana pardalina* is related both to the age and phase of the mother (Matthée, 1951). Old females of the phase *transiens-gregaria* usually lay more diapause eggs than young females. But phase far outweighs the slight effect of age. On average, *gregaria* females lay 42 % of diapause eggs, *transiens* 72 % and *solitaria* 100 %.

CHAPTER 3

THE INHERITANCE OF DIAPAUSE

MANY insects have geographical races that differ in the character of their diapause. In some species strains with facultative and obligatory diapause occur; in others additional strains are known that are entirely free of diapause. Since both these forms of arrest, and the freedom from diapause, are an expression of the hereditary make-up of the insect, the basis of inheritance of these conditions can be examined by the normal methods of genetical analysis. However, from the standpoint of developmental physiology it is also of interest to discover what Ephrussi (1939) has called the 'point of attack' of the genotype. In the case of an insect with facultative diapause, the perception of the environmental stimulus is merely the first of a series of processes which eventually lead to the arrest of growth. Some of these intermediate steps are known, although others still await definition (see Chapter 8). The insect with obligatory diapause is often regarded as indifferent to the environment. The implication is therefore that the receptor mechanism is not required for the initiation of this train of events. Our main concern in the present chapter is to draw attention to the opposite possibility, namely, that this mechanism is present and fully functional but that the insect responds to so wide a range of environmental conditions that it can rarely escape diapause. If this be the case, it is to the performance of the receptor rather than to some later process that one must look for the 'point of attack' of the genotype.

The Inheritance of Diapause

THE EFFECT OF THE ENVIRONMENT ON INSECTS
WITH OBLIGATORY DIAPAUSE

Although information on this subject is scanty, it is clear that at least some species with obligatory diapause are not entirely shielded from the environment. Certain Lepidoptera belonging to the family Orgyidae sometimes fail to enter diapause under extreme conditions of temperature, even though they normally observe a very strict univoltine rhythm in nature. The embryonic diapause in *Orgyia antiqua* is almost completely stable. No eggs escape this condition when *Orgyia* is reared at temperatures within the range 15–25° C.; but moths lay about 3 % of non-diapause eggs if they have been exposed as pupae to temperatures as high as 30° C. *Olene fascelina*, a species with an obligatory larval diapause, is scarcely affected even by a temperature of 32° C., although this proves lethal to many of the larvae. However, a second species, *Leucoma salicis*, yields to temperatures near the limits of tolerance, some 60 % of the larvae developing without interruption at 30° C. (Kozhantshikov, 1948). In this species, also, up to 53 % of the larvae escape diapause when reared with a photoperiod of 20 hours, although diapause is universal with all other light régimes (Gayspitz, 1953).

It could perhaps be argued that this response to temperature is unconnected with the receptor mechanism and that some later process in the normal sequence is set off by high temperature. However, this possibility can be excluded in *Bombyx* since the same response may be observed with low temperature—a normal diapause-preventing stimulus in this species. When the eggs are incubated at 15° C., up to 31 % of the moths belonging to the Chinese univoltine strains lay diapause egg batches. Under identical conditions the 'stronger' univoltine race Japanese no. 1 yields only 7·5 % of non-diapause batches, while the European univoltine strains produce between 1 and 10 % (Umeya, 1926).

41

THE GENETICS OF DIAPAUSE IN *BOMBYX MORI*

Univoltine, bivoltine and quadrivoltine races, as well as 'multivoltine' strains entirely free of diapause, are known in the silkworm. The early genetical studies of Toyama (1912) and Tanaka (1924) established that the voltinism of the egg, like other characters such as colour and shape, was determined by the genetic constitution of the mother and was independent of the race of the male parent. But a comprehensive analysis of the genetics of diapause only became possible after the role of temperature and photoperiod had been defined by Watanabe (1918, 1919, cited in Kuwana, 1932) and Kogure (1933).

According to the recent work of Nagatomo (quoted in Tanaka, 1953) three sex-linked alleles, $+^{Hs}$, Hs^2 and Hs, and three autosomal genes, H_1, H_2 and H_3, are concerned in the inheritance of voltinism. The sex-linked genes show complete epistasis in the order $Hs > Hs_2 > +^{Hs}$, while the effect of the autosomal dominants is cumulative and proportional to their number. The following arbitrary 'hibernating values' (H.V.) have been assigned to these genes:

$$Hs = 6; \quad Hs^2 = 3; \quad +^{Hs} = 0,$$
$$H_1 = 1; \quad H_2 = 1; \quad H_3 = 1.$$

The genetic constitution of the different strains can be represented as follows:

Univoltines: $Hs\,H_1\,H_1\,H_2\,H_2\,H_3\,H_3$ (H.V. = 12),
Bivoltines: $Hs^2\,H_1\,H_1 +^{H_2} +^{H_2} +^{H_3} +^{H_3}$ (H.V. = 5),
Multivoltines: $+^{Hs} +^{H_1} +^{H_1} +^{H_2} +^{H_2} +^{H_3} +^{H_3}$ (H.V. = 0).

The results of hybridizing univoltine and bivoltine races may be given as a typical example. The female is the heterogametic sex:

$$\text{U (12) } ♀ \times \text{B (5) } ♂$$

F_1 ♀ (7) $\qquad\qquad$ ♂ (10)
$(Hs^2\,H_1\,H_1\,H_2 +^{H_2} H_3 +^{H_3})$ $\quad$ $(Hs\,Hs^2\,H_1\,H_1\,H_2 +^{H_2} H_3 +^{H_3})$

$$\text{B (5) } ♀ \times \text{U (12) } ♂$$

F_1 ♀ (10) $\qquad\qquad$ ♂ (10)
$(Hs\,H_1\,H_1 +^{H_2} H_2 +^{H_3} H_3)$ $\quad$ $(Hs\,Hs^2\,H_1\,H_1 +^{H_2} H_2 +^{H_3} H_3)$

It will be observed that in the strength of their voltinism the F_1 females are intermediate between the two parental races, although the daughters produced by reciprocal matings are not alike in this respect. Those obtained from the first cross are bivoltine, but if they have been reared from the egg stage at low temperatures they lay rather more diapause egg batches than moths belonging to the bivoltine race of the male parent. In the reciprocal cross the F_1 females are weak univoltines. By suitable recombination experiments a graded series of hybrid moths can be produced with hibernating values ranging from 0 to 12. The grade of female is recognized by the reaction to the incubation temperature:

0–1   Non-diapause eggs are laid at all temperatures.

2–4   Non-diapause eggs are laid over most of the temperature range, but some moths produce diapause egg batches after incubation at high temperatures.

5–7   Typical bivoltines. Non-diapause eggs are laid at low, and diapause eggs at high temperatures.

8–10 Diapause eggs are laid over most of the temperature range but some moths produce non-diapause egg batches after incubation at low temperatures.

11–12 Diapause eggs are laid at all temperatures.

It has been possible to evolve two strains with equal hibernating values but different genotypes. The first carries the gene *Hs*, while the second is homozygous for all three autosomal dominants. Both strains therefore have a H.V. of 6 and respond in a similar manner to temperature. But the reciprocal crosses between these strains give entirely different results. F_1 hybrid females with a H.V. of 3 are produced when the gene *Hs* is derived from the mother, but one of 9 if this gene has been borne by the father.

Similar differences doubtless occur in commercial silkworm races. For example, the Chinese bivoltine races still tend to produce some non-diapause egg batches at high temperatures, whereas the 'stronger' Japanese bivoltines do not (Umeya, 1926). And similar differences among univoltine races have already been noted. There can be little doubt that the mode of action of the genotype is to modify the reaction of the receptors to external factors such as temperature. In *Bombyx*, as in other insects, there is gradual transition over the effective temperature scale from temperatures that are diapause-inducing to those which are diapause-preventing (see Chapter 2). In the univoltine races the range which is normally diapause-inducing (in the bivoltine races) is widened and extended to much lower temperatures so that diapause becomes virtually obligatory (fig. 9). The reverse process must of course be imagined in the

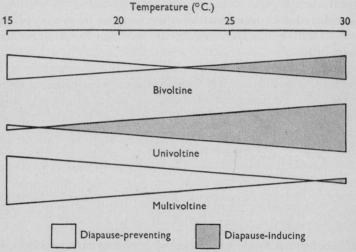

Fig. 9. Diagram illustrating the shift in the response to temperature in different races of *Bombyx mori*. For further explanation, see text.

multivoltine strains. The secondary failure of diapause in the latter is evidently not due to any other physiological 'defect', for most of the so-called multivoltine races will produce some diapause eggs if subjected to extremely high temperatures.

The status of the quadrivoltine strains, which some Japanese authors regard as possessing a lower 'hibernating value' than the bivoltines, is more difficult to assess. Kogure's (1933) experiments with the quadrivoltine race *Tsunomata* suggests that the temperature and day-length response is much the same as in the bivoltine races *Showa* and *Shohoku*. In all three races diapause is of the usual facultative type and can be induced or prevented in any generation by the appropriate external conditions. There can therefore be no suggestion that any hypothetical 'hibernation' substance is accumulated and transmitted to the next generation. The rate of larval development is known to be considerably more rapid in the quadrivoltine than in the other races. But this in itself seems insufficient to account for the interpolation of two extra generations in the normal annual cycle.

DIAPAUSE AS A RACIAL CHARACTER IN
OTHER INSECTS

There are many species in which the number of annual generations varies regularly in different parts of the geographical range. In some cases the characteristic pattern seems to be maintained solely by the operation of the environment (see p. 125). However, natural selection has often tended to favour the evolution of genetic strains which respond differently to the environment. In such species both heredity and environment are concerned in the determination of the voltinism.

The cornborer *Pyrausta nubilalis* is a familiar example. This species is widely distributed in Europe where well-defined one-generation and two-generation areas can be recognized. For example, *Pyrausta* is predominantly univoltine in Hungary, Russia, northern Yugoslavia and northern France, and bivoltine in the southern part of its range which includes the Po valley, southern Yugoslavia and the Mediterranean seaboard of France (Babcock, 1927 *b*; Babcock and Vance, 1929).

Outbreaks of the cornborer in the United States were first discovered in Massachusetts (New England) in 1917 and near New York four years later (Vance, 1942). It soon became evident that the populations in these areas represented distinct biological races, probably originating from separate introductions. In the north-eastern (Lake) States *Pyrausta* completed only one generation a year, while in New England it was bivoltine. When the single-generation strain was reared in New England, the univoltine life cycle was maintained for four successive seasons, showing that at the time of this investigation diapause was obligatory (Barber, 1925). On the other hand, the generation number in the New England strain was clearly determined by the environment, for larvae hatching late in the season were found to pass through only one generation (O'Kane and Lowry, 1927). Arbuthnot (1944) has since shown that the cornborer population in Connecticut (New England) is homozygous for multiple generations (that is, for facultative diapause). In contrast, the diapause character of the Ohio (Lake States) population has changed significantly in recent years and now includes both single and multiple generation strains which interbreed in the field (see also p. 130).

Similar geographical races have been described in the European spruce sawfly by Prebble (1941c). *Gilpinia polytoma* has one generation in the Gaspé peninsular of Quebec but completes two generations in New Brunswick and three as far south as Connecticut. Obligatory diapause predominates in the north, facultative diapause in the south—a relationship which is also probable in *Telea polyphemus* (Dawson, 1931).

The situation is more complex in the case of the migratory locust *Locusta migratoria*. The tropical subspecies *migratorioides* always develops without arrest, but races possessing diapause are found near the northerly limits of the area of distribution where moderate or even severe winters are encountered, for example, in France (Le Berre, 1953 and personal communication) and in southern Russia (Yakhimovich, 1950). The distribution of these races is surprisingly local. In the South of France alone, three distinct races can be recognized: (1) In the subspecies *gallica* from the Bordeaux region about 94% of the eggs exhibit a firm diapause and fail to hatch at 33° C. unless they are first chilled. 1% develop without interruption, taking about 14 days at 33° C.; and 5% are of intermediate type, eventually hatching after a delay which may vary between 37 and 156 days. The proportion of diapause and non-diapause eggs is not influenced by the temperature at which the locusts are reared. The distinction therefore is between obligatory diapause and the absence of diapause. This subspecies is migratory. (2) A second race, distinct from *gallica*, is found in the Midi in the region of Montpellier. In this instance diapause is facultative, for although eggs of both types are laid, the proportions are much altered by temperature. (3) A third subspecies, *canescens*, occurs in the Department of Var near the Italian border. This race is entirely without diapause but differs from *migratorioides* in being non-migratory.

The Inheritance of Diapause

Although the evolution of such racial complexes is usually associated with isolation in the geographical sense, this is not invariably so. When 'ecological speciation' has taken place, strains differing in the diapause character are sometimes found existing side by side on different host plants. Thus in Swiss populations of the mite *Bryobia*, it is possible to distinguish a multivoltine strain with a facultative egg diapause which feeds on apple, a univoltine strain on gooseberry and a strain lacking a diapause which is confined to ivy (Mathys, 1954).

SELECTION FOR AN ENVIRONMENTAL RESPONSE

It may be recalled that in *Bombyx* a graded series of phenotypes can be traced ranging from univoltine strains with obligatory diapause, through bivoltine strains with facultative diapause to multivoltine strains virtually free of diapause. And there is clear evidence that genetic control is exercised through a shift in reaction of the receptor mechanism to the environmental factor. Selection experiments with other insects also throw light on this question.

Working with the subspecies *gallica* of *Locusta migratoria* Le Berre (1953) was able to isolate two strains, the first with a uniform and obligatory diapause and the second entirely free of diapause. The course of events during the first three generations of one selection line is shown in fig. 10. The rapid progress of selection in the direction of freedom from diapause is indicated both by the increase in the proportion of eggs which develop without interruption and also by the fall in the incubation time of eggs of 'intermediate' type. Complete freedom from diapause was secured after six generations. Some selection experiments have also been carried out with the Montpellier strain. Locusts from this population lay fewer diapause eggs at 33° C. than at lower temperatures. While it has proved possible to select a line which would produce no diapause eggs at 33° C., these insects still yielded some diapause eggs at lower temperatures.

These observations may perhaps be interpreted as follows. The slow progress of selection in the Montpellier strain suggests that many genes are concerned and that these modify the

47

environmental response in only small steps. It is possible nevertheless that with continued selection a strain could eventually
be built up that was without diapause over the whole temperature range; and conversely, selection in the opposite direction

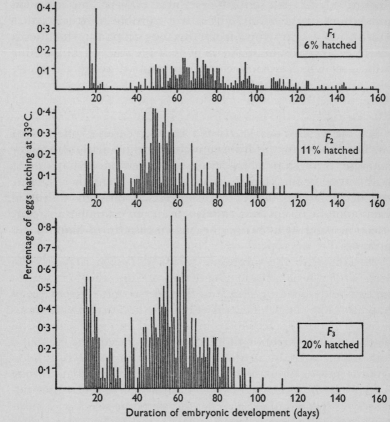

Fig. 10. Charts showing the incidence and intensity of diapause in a line of
Locusta migratoria selected for freedom from diapause (after Le Berre). The histograms indicate the percentages of eggs hatching daily at 33° C. without preliminary
chilling in three successive generations of the selection line. The total numbers of
eggs that hatched are given on the right.

might be expected to yield a strain with obligatory diapause at
all temperatures. The genetic control of diapause in the subspecies *gallica* may be exercised in a similar fashion. The difference will arise from the fact that the population carries a set

of genes (perhaps relatively few in number) which exerts a far
more profound effect upon the environmental response. The
progress of selection in this population is therefore correspondingly rapid.

Some modification in the temperature response has also been
recorded in a strain of *Ephestia elutella* with obligatory diapause
(Waloff, 1949). By repeatedly breeding from the few moths
which escaped diapause at high temperature a strain was
evolved that developed without interruption at 25° C. However, in this case the range of temperatures which were diapause-
preventing had not been extended far down the temperature
scale for 92 % of the larvae entered diapause at 21° C.

The response to day length is also subject to the influence of
selection. Although univoltine races are unknown in the silkmoth *Antheraea pernyi*, Tanaka (1951 b) has demonstrated that
most bivoltine stocks of commercial origin contain sufficient
genetic variability for the conversion to be accomplished.
A univoltine strain with virtually obligatory diapause was ultimately secured by selecting for high incidence of diapause at
constant long photoperiods.

CHAPTER 4

THE ENVIRONMENT AND THE
TERMINATION OF DIAPAUSE

MANY insects in a state of diapause die without developing or
grow in a protracted and irregular manner when exposed to
temperatures that would be expected to favour morphogenesis.
On the other hand, their subsequent growth is often promoted
by exposure to temperatures that are too low to permit the
growth of the non-diapause stages. These are among the
most striking features of the diapause condition. Since it has
been known for many years that temperature shocks and
other stimuli sometimes cause growth to be resumed, diapause
has often been regarded as a state of blocked or inhibited
development which must be 'broken' by the stimulus of cold.
A more profitable approach to this question has been made by
Andrewartha (1952), who has suggested that the events preceding the resumption of growth can be looked upon as a process of gradual development which is influenced by temperature
in much the same fashion as morphogenesis.

Andrewartha (1943, 1952) has illustrated this conception by
reference to the eggs of *Austroicetes cruciata*. If the diapause eggs
of this South Australian plague grasshopper are chilled for
60 days at 10° C., they hatch promptly and uniformly when
subsequently incubated at 25° C. (fig. 11A). The same period of
chilling at 6 or 13·5° C. is much less effective and fewer eggs
hatch when incubated at high temperature. Nevertheless, complete and uniform development can still be secured if the period
of chilling is extended beyond 60 days. At temperatures much
lower than 5° C. or higher than 25° C. the eggs always fail to
hatch however long the exposure. These responses to temperature show that the termination of diapause can be regarded as
a developmental process which is completed most rapidly at a
temperature optimum of 10° C. but which is also eventually

50

completed more slowly at other temperatures falling within the the effective range. This process, for which Andrewartha coined the term 'diapause development', can either be expressed as a duration or as the reciprocal, the rate of development. The term refers of course to physiological development; although slow morphological development takes place in the diapause egg of *Austroicetes* (p. 10), this is exceptional.

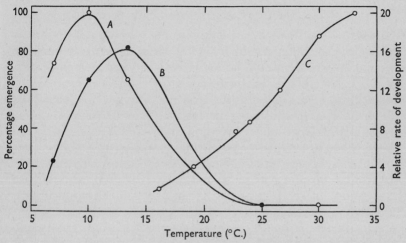

Fig. 11. The influence of temperature on diapause development and morphogenesis in *Austroicetes cruciata* (after Andrewartha). A, eggs from South Australia. B, eggs from West Australia. Left-hand ordinate shows the proportion of eggs to complete diapause development during 60 days at the temperature specified. C and right-hand ordinate show the relative rates of development of the post-diapause embryos at different temperatures.

Bombyx is a second insect in which the effect of temperature on the rate of completion of diapause is known in considerable detail. These trends are shown in fig. 12 which is based on the data of Muroga (1951). The thermal optimum is about 7° C. Eggs which have been kept warm for 30 days after laying require only 60–70 days of chilling at 5° C. before 90 % will hatch at higher incubation temperatures; but at 2·5° C. 80 days are required, at 12·5° C. over 100 and at 15° C. nearly 160. Diapause disappears so slowly at 0 or 17·5° C. that only 11 % of the eggs hatched after 200 days at the latter temperature. This factor is regarded by Muroga as influencing the rate

4-2

of consumption of a hypothetical inhibitory substance, but Andrewartha's interpretation is preferable.

If the low-temperature treatment is continued after diapause development has been completed the arrest of growth will persist, provided the temperature is below the threshold of morpho-

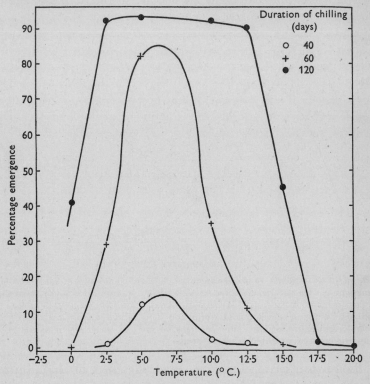

Fig. 12. The influence of temperature on the rate of termination of diapause in *Bombyx mori* (after Muroga). The ordinate shows the percentages of eggs which hatched at the incubation temperature (22·5° C.) after they had been chilled for 40, 60 or 120 days at the temperature specified. In all cases the eggs were stored for 30 days at 25° C. prior to the low-temperature treatment.

genesis. The quiescent insect may remain alive for a considerable period. In the silkworm egg there is no hint that viability is reduced at 5° C. even though the eggs are exposed to 5° C. for 50 or so days longer than is necessary to complete diapause development (fig. 12). In the ichneumonid *Exeristes roborator*, an external parasite of *Pyrausta*, dormancy is ended in 80 days at a temperature of 0–2° C. But even after 540 days at this temperature 88 % of the 5th-instar larvae still pupate successfully at 27° C. (Baker and Jones, 1934). In general, however, viability gradually falls if post-diapause growth is prevented. For example, when the eggs of *Lymantria dispar* are exposed to a temperature ranging from − 2 to + 2° C. they become free of diapause after about 8 months; yet after 14 months at this temperature mortality is almost complete (Kozhantshikov, 1950a).

We shall now turn to consider the role of temperature in greater detail. Although this factor is by far the most important environmental agency controlling the termination of diapause, day length and sometimes other factors may also be influential in some species.

THE TEMPERATURE REQUIREMENTS FOR DIAPAUSE DEVELOPMENT: THE RANGE AND OPTIMUM

In *Austroicetes* the temperature range over which diapause development can proceed is comparatively narrow. Nevertheless, the upper limits just overlap the threshold for morphogenesis, so that within this intermediate range diapause development and morphogenesis can take place concurrently (fig. 11). In other species of grasshoppers with diapause eggs the effective temperature range for diapause development is much wider and indeed extends to all temperatures at which morphogenesis can occur. Some feature, such as the delay in the resumption of growth, rather than the proportion of individuals developing, must then be selected as an index of the completion of diapause development. The eggs of *Melanoplus mexicanus* hatch at all temperatures up to 37° C. But low temperatures are evidently more influential than high in ending diapause, for the incubation period at 37° C. is 46 days whereas this becomes reduced to 11 days if the freshly laid eggs are first chilled for 240 days at 0° C. (Parker, 1930). The eggs of *M. differentialis* require a mean incubation period of 89 days at 23° C. and of 28 days at 30° C. But after exposure to outdoor winter conditions for 168 days the eggs hatch promptly in only 12 days when incubated at 23° C. (Bodine, 1925).

When growth is resumed at all temperatures over the morphogenetic range it is still possible to gauge the rate of disappearance of diapause by permitting some diapause development first at the higher temperature and then estimating the duration of low temperature needed to reduce the incubation period to the minimum. By this means Church and Salt (1952) found that in *M. bivittatus* diapause was terminated three to four times more rapidly at 5 than at 25° C. In spite of the wide range of effective temperatures in these species of *Melanoplus*, the temperature optimum is probably a few degrees lower than in *Austroicetes*.

Insects show great diversity in their thermal requirements for diapause development. The close connexion of these physiological requirements with climate and geographical distribution has been studied particularly by Danilyevsky (1949). An excellent illustration of this principle is provided by the following series of saturniid moths: *Saturnia pavonia*, *Antheraea pernyi*, *Philosamia cynthia*, *P. ricini*. The first is a Palaearctic species extending as far north as the Arctic Circle; the second, the Tussor silkmoth, is native to China; the two species of *Philosamia* are subtropical, the area of distribution in the wild state extending from India into southern China and Indo-Malay. The first three insects enter diapause as pupae; the last is without diapause.

Reference to fig. 13 shows that the temperature range most favourable for larval growth and imaginal differentiation (*c*. 15–32° C.) hardly differs even in the extreme members of the series. Yet the temperatures at which diapause disappears differ in a most striking manner. In *Saturnia* the most effective range (*c*. −15 to 7° C.) is far below the threshold of morphogenesis; this species can therefore never develop in constant thermal conditions. In *Antheraea* the range is higher, extending from about −5 to almost 15° C. The temperature optimum is approximately 10° C. (Zolotarev, 1947). In *Philosamia cynthia* the ranges for diapause development (*c*. 0–25° C.) and morphogenesis overlap broadly but are by no means identical.

The thermal requirements of the diapause stage in other insects can best be considered in the light of these results. Some insects which are normally subjected to severe winter conditions clearly require comparatively low temperatures. In the tent caterpillar *Malacosoma disstria* a temperature of 2° C. is most influential in terminating the embryonic diapause. Although the rate of diapause development falls off abruptly below the thermal optimum, it still remains appreciable at − 5° C. Above the optimum the curve declines more gradually towards the upper limit of *c.* 20° C. (Hodson and Weinman, 1945). In the sawfly *Gilpinia polytoma*, an inhabitant of the spruce forests of

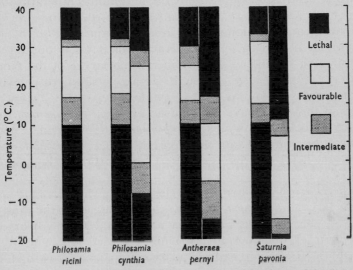

Fig. 13. Histograms showing the thermal requirements for diapause development and for morphogenesis in four species of saturniid moths (after Danilyevsky).

Europe and Canada, diapause can be completed at − 10° C.; and a temperature of 10° C. is too high for satisfactory development (Prebble, 1941 *b*).

Many insects from temperate climates with moderately severe winters have been found to respond most readily to temperatures within the general range 0–12° C. The thermal requirements of the diapause eggs of *Bombyx* have already been mentioned. The optimum temperature is 7° C. and the effective temperature range approximately 0–17° C. (Muroga, 1951; Zolotarev and Popel, 1947). In the eggs of the fall cankerworm *Alsophila pometaria* diapause development proceeds most rapidly at 10° C.

and cannot be completed at temperatures much lower than 1° C. or higher than 22° C. (Flemion and Hartzell, 1936). Temperatures of 5 and 10° C. are about equally effective in the eggs of *Melanoplus differentialis* and are more favourable than 0 and 15° C. (Burdick, 1937).

Many European Lepidoptera which enter diapause as larvae or pupae also respond most rapidly to temperatures within this range. In species such as *Phalera bucephala*, *Smerinthus ocellatus*, *S. ligustri* and *Loxostege sticticalis* the optimum temperature lies close to, or just above, 0° C. (Danilyevsky, 1949). Above 15° C. diapause continues for at least one year and in *Phalera* may persist for 2–3 years. A temperature of 8° C. is optimal in terminating dormancy in the hibernating larvae of the pierid butterfly *Aporia crataegi*, although diapause is slowly dispelled at temperatures as low as −5° C. (Zolotarev, 1950). Temperatures of this order have also proved effective in *Timarcha tenebricosa* (Abeloos, 1935), *Cydia pomonella* (Townsend, 1926), *Grapholitha molesta* (van Steenburgh, 1929), *Drosophila nitens* (Bertani, 1947) and *Agelastica alni* (Chrysomelidae) (Beaumont, 1944).

The progress of diapause development in the dormant 3rd-instar larva of *Epistrophe bifasciata* can be judged by the dimensions of the eye disks and other anlage; their growth at the inception of diapause is far more retarded than in other Syrphids that develop without a larval diapause. Growth of the eye disks is negligible at temperatures as low as 0·4° C. or as high as 25° C. The maximal rate of growth occurs at 9–10° C., a temperature which is also most favourable for bringing the arrest to an end (Schneider, 1948).

The diapause stages of insects from warmer environments require correspondingly higher temperatures. In the eggs of the cricket *Gryllulus commodus* the rate of completion of diapause is maximal at 13° C.; the effective range extends from 8 to *c.* 27° C. (Browning, 1952*b*). These requirements are adjusted to the relatively mild winters of South Australia. The larvae of the carpet beetle *Anthrenus verbasci* (Dermestidae) grow and pupate more rapidly at 20° C. than at higher or lower temperatures (Kuwana, 1951).

The thermal optimum is considerably higher in the moth

Diparopsis castanea. This indigenous multivoltine noctuid is an important pest of cotton in Nyasaland and elsewhere in the southern monsoon belt of tropical Africa. Although tempera-

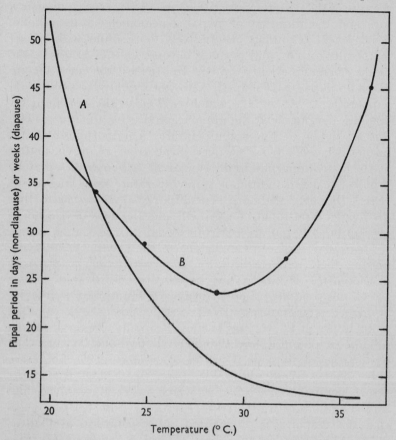

Fig. 14. The influence of temperature on the duration of the pupal stage in *Diparopsis castanea* (after Pearson). A, non-diapause pupa. B, diapause pupa. *Note.* 80% of the diapause pupae incubated at 37° C. had still failed to emerge after 51 weeks; in order to include this point on the graph this has been assumed to represent the full span of the pupal period in these individuals.

tures during the period of pupal dormancy fall somewhat below the average for the year, the function of diapause in this species is to span a period of drought when the annual growth of the host plant is at an end (Pearson and Mitchell, 1945).

The effect of temperature on the rate of development of the 'long-term' and 'short-term' pupae is illustrated in fig. 14 (Pearson, personal communication). It will be noted that in the case of the non-diapause pupae the curve relating temperature and the duration of pupal development is hyperbolic, development becoming progressively more rapid with rise of temperature up to, and perhaps beyond, 37° C. At 28° C. the moths emerge in about 16 days. In contrast, the curve for the diapause pupae is U-shaped. Growth is relatively slow at all temperatures. At 28° C., which is close to the optimum for diapause development, the pupal stage lasts for about 24 weeks. But at higher or lower temperatures metamorphosis is still further delayed. At 19° C. over 38 weeks are required, and at 37° C. many pupae fail to develop at all, although they may be kept in a healthy condition at this temperature for as long as two years. *Diparopsis* therefore resembles *Philosamia cynthia* in that the temperature ranges for growth and diapause development overlap broadly but are not coincident.

Leptinotarsa also seems to belong to the group of insects requiring high temperatures for the completion of diapause development. If hibernating beetles are chilled at 0–5, 7 or 12° C. this treatment merely delays the resumption of activity at higher temperatures. If they are exposed to a constant temperature of 25° C., the beetles eventually emerge from the soil in 2 or 3 months, and then begin to feed and lay eggs. The termination of diapause is still more rapid at 30° C., requiring only about 3 weeks (de Wilde, 1949, 1953). The eggs of the brown locust *Locustana pardalina*, which must endure the hot and arid conditions of the Karroo Desert, may also belong to this class, for diapause is terminated at temperatures as high as 35° C. (Matthée, 1951). The Californian zygaenid *Harrisina brillians* is probably a further example (Smith and Langston, 1953).

THE DURATION OF DIAPAUSE

The rate of completion of diapause often varies widely in different individuals of the same species. For example, in *Melanoplus bivittatus*, the mean period required for diapause development at the thermal optimum (5° C.) is 40 days; nevertheless, some eggs are free of diapause after only a few days while others require nearly 100 days (Church and Salt, 1952). In spite of this variability, the duration of diapause is an important diagnostic feature which provides a measure of the 'intensity' of diapause in the species.

In some insects the arrest is very transient. Hibernating adults of the pentatomid *Eurydema ventralis* cannot readily be induced to feed, copulate and lay fertile eggs if kept at high temperatures; but exposure to a temperature of 8° C. for only 9 days suffices to terminate their dormancy (Bonnemaison, 1952). Freshly laid diapause eggs of *Gryllulus commodus* require only 15 days at 13° C. for the completion of diapause development (Browning, 1952 a). If the eggs of *Melanoplus mexicanus* are first allowed partial development at 22° C. (see p. 62), 30 days at 0° C. are adequate to reduce the mean incubation period to the minimal value (Parker, 1930).

We have seen that diapause is somewhat more intense in the eggs of *Bombyx*. The arrest can be ended in 60 days at 5° C. if the low-temperature treatment is begun within 30 days of egg-laying (Muroga, 1951). Larvae of the wheat-stem sawfly *Cephus cinctus* must spend 90–100 days at the thermal optimum (c. 10° C.) before 95 % will pupate at 25° C. (Salt, 1947). The winter eggs of *Metatetranychus ulmi* need 150–200 days at 1 or 6° C. before growth can be resumed at 25° C. (Lees, 1953 a).

The arrest of growth sometimes persists for more than 1 year. Moths have emerged from the dormant pupae of *Rothschildia jorulla* after 8 years (Rowley, 1923), and from those of *Eriogaster lanestris* and *Biston alpinus* after 6 or 7 years (Standfuss, 1896; Danilyevsky, 1951). In the walnut fly *Rhagoletis completa* two-thirds of the pupae yield adults after 1 year, but a small proportion remain in the soil without developing for up to 4 years (Boyce, 1931). In the tortricid *Melissopus* 82 % of the larvae entering diapause in any one year were found to overwinter once, 13 % twice and 5 % three times (Dohanion, 1942). In the bivoltine race of *Gilpinia polytoma* from New Brunswick the emergence of the sawflies is complete by the third spring after the 5th-stage larvae have dropped to the forest floor and spun a cocoon. Diapause is even more intense in the predominantly univoltine population from Nova Scotia, some prepupae lying dormant for 6 years (table 4) (Prebble, 1941*e*). The wheat blossom midge *Sitodiplosis mosellana* is remarkable in passing up to twelve winters in the soil, although nearly one-third of the diapausing larvae which enter the soil in any one season pupate after only one winter (Barnes, 1943, 1952).

TABLE 4. *The intensity of diapause in populations of the spruce sawfly* Gilpinia polytoma *collected in one-generation (Gaspé) and two-generation areas (New Brunswick) (from Prebble). The table shows the percentages of prepupae resuming development in each subsequent year*

Locality	Year					
	1	2	3	4	5	6
Gaspé	49	9	23	18	0·9	0·04
New Brunswick	65	24	11	—	—	—

These instances of long-enduring diapause would clearly repay further study by experimental methods. The duration of the arrest will of course be extended in nature if the environmental conditions fail to tally with the thermal requirements of the diapause stage. However, it is more probable that these insects are characterized by an intense diapause so that the arrest is terminated extremely slowly even at the thermal optimum. Whether this can be regarded as a cumulative process or whether the amount of diapause development completed after one winter is 'lost' before the succeeding winter is not known. Nor has any explanation been offered of the striking individual variations which affect the duration of diapause. As some selective advantage may accrue from the faculty of spreading emergence over several years, the basis of this heterogeneity may perhaps be genetical.

THE PERIOD OF SENSITIVITY TO LOW TEMPERATURE

We have seen above that diapause is brought to an end with greatest expedition when the insect is exposed to the optimum temperature. In many insect eggs, and in those of Orthoptera in particular, there is a second requirement, namely, that this temperature régime should synchronize with some definite stage in the morphological or physiological development of the embryo.

The timing of the sensitive period has been carefully studied by Andrewartha (1943) in *Austroicetes*. In this particular species the period of sensitivity can be defined in relation to the stages of morphogenesis, since the embryo continues to grow slowly throughout anatrepsis. The most rapid response to low temperature occurs at the close of anatrepsis. At this time an exposure for 60 days at the thermal optimum (10° C.) serves to terminate diapause in every egg. In order, however, that the embryo may grow to this stage, the eggs must first be exposed to temperatures above the threshold for growth. In Andrewartha's experiments this was achieved with a régime of alternating low (10° C.) and high (25° C.) temperatures lasting 40 days.

If the low-temperature treatment is given either too early or too late, the egg may never become competent to resume active development. For example, eggs which have just entered diapause at the beginning of anatrepsis are unaffected by low temperature, even when the exposure lasts as long as 116 days. On the other hand, preliminary high-temperature treatments that allow the embryo to grow past the sensitive stage result in the intensification of diapause. Much longer exposures to low temperature are then needed to end the arrest. There are also signs of morphological abnormality. The embryos become unusually large, revolution may fail and many monsters are produced.

In other insect eggs the sensitive period may come before the embryo has entered the morphological diapause stage, at the inception of diapause, or even some considerable time after embryonic growth has ceased. The period of sensitivity can therefore be related more appropriately to the stages of physiological rather than of morphological development.

The eggs of *Gryllulus commodus* are most responsive to low temperature immediately after they are laid, that is, several days before they actually enter diapause (Browning, 1952a). A 15-day exposure to a temperature of 13° C. then suffices to dispel the state of diapause. On subsequent incubation at higher temperatures the embryos develop promptly and without interruption—the eggs therefore never suffer an arrest at the normal morphological diapause stage. Low temperature is much less effective if the treatment is delayed until the eggs have entered diapause. A period of nearly 60 days is then required for the completion of diapause development at 13° C.

A similar temperature sequence is also effective in *Melanoplus bivittatus*. Freshly laid eggs that have been chilled for an adequate period develop without interruption when incubated at higher temperatures (Church and Salt, 1952). Diapause is also

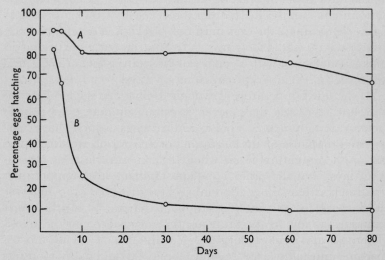

Fig. 15. The effect of different temperature treatments on the completion of diapause in *Bombyx mori* (after Muroga). The abscissa shows the duration of the initial exposure to 25° C. before the eggs were chilled at 5° C. In A the eggs were chilled for 60 days and in B for 40 days.

averted when the eggs of *M. mexicanus* are chilled in the early stages of embryogenesis; nevertheless in this species the rate of completion of diapause is distinctly more rapid if the eggs are first permitted to develop partially at higher temperatures (Parker, 1930).

It will be recalled that in *Bombyx* growth is suspended at a relatively early stage of embryogenesis (p. 9). The effect of low temperature seems to become most decisive at about this time (*c.* 30 hours after the egg is laid). If the eggs are incubated

at 25° C. without preliminary chilling, diapause becomes progressively more intense. This feature is illustrated in fig. 15
which is constructed from the data of Muroga (1951). The effect
is of course most striking if the period of chilling is short and
therefore of critical duration. In one treatment the eggs were
subjected to a temperature of 5° C. for 40 days (fig. 15 B). The
percentage reactivated then declined from 84 to 8 % as the
initial exposure to high temperature was extended from 3 to
80 days.*

The diapause egg of *Locusta migratoria gallica* differs from the
preceding examples in that the period of greatest sensitivity to
cold occurs long after embryonic growth has been arrested (Le
Berre, 1953). The following is the most favourable régime for
terminating diapause: 60 days at 25° C., then 60 days at 8° C.,
then 33° C. At a temperature of 25° C. the embryo requires
10 days to grow to the morphological diapause stage, which in
this species occurs at the end of anatrepsis just prior to the
revolution of the embryo. No further morphological development can take place at this temperature which is outside the
range at which diapause development can proceed. Low-
temperature treatments are wholly ineffective if applied immediately after the egg is laid or when the embryo has just
entered diapause after 10 days. However, from this point
onwards the egg becomes increasingly responsive to chilling and
eventually becomes maximally sensitive about 50 days after
growth has ceased.

EVIDENCE FOR MULTIPLE THERMAL REACTIONS

Although 'diapause development' has so far been regarded as
a unitary process, it is unlikely that any simple chemical reaction would proceed more rapidly at low than at moderately
high temperatures within the biological range. The mechanism
of diapause development may be pictured with greater
probability as depending on the interaction of two or more

* In apparent contrast, Emme (1949a) observed a progressive increase in
the sensitivity of *Bombyx* eggs to chilling when they were incubated initially
at 22° C, for periods ranging up to 200 days. Perhaps, however, this
temperature just falls within the upper limit for diapause development.

processes which have different positive temperature coefficients and which compete for the same substrate. The existence of a series of linked reactions could not be detected if the system as a whole operated unchanged throughout the entire diapause period. But any well-marked change in the thermal optimum would be indicative of the complexity of 'diapause development'. Such trends have sometimes been observed. The eggs of *Locusta migratoria* afford one of the most striking examples. As we have already noted, the first phase of diapause development is completed more rapidly at 25° C., the second phase at 8° C.

In some species there are indications that the final stages of diapause development can be completed at higher temperatures than the first. This conclusion is implicit in the results obtained by Hodson and Weinman (1945) with *Malacosoma*. When the eggs were exposed to a temperature of 2° C. for 3 months 93 % subsequently hatched at 25° C.; the mean incubation period was then 12 days. After the eggs had been chilled for 6 months, 95 % hatched promptly after a mean incubation period of only 5 days. This must mean that diapause development was not entirely complete after 3 months of chilling even though almost every egg was able eventually to resume development. Since the eggs of *Malacosoma* never hatch at a constant temperature of 25° C., the final, but not the initial, stages of diapause development can evidently be completed at this temperature.

Browning (1952 *b*) has also shown with the eggs of *Gryllulus* that the thermal requirements for initiating post-diapause growth vary according to the amount of diapause development that has previously been completed at low temperatures. In general, the smaller the amount, the higher the incubation temperature needed to provoke growth. For example, eggs that had been chilled for 30 days at 10° C.—a régime which permits partial diapause development—always failed to develop when incubated at 21° C., but 64 and 84 % respectively hatched promptly at incubation temperatures of 26·5 and 30° C. The thermal optimum during the final stages of diapause development must then be far higher than during the initial stages.

The Environment and the Termination of Diapause

In most insects with facultative diapause the agencies which induce diapause cease to exert any action once growth has been arrested. They are indeed entirely divorced from the processes—often as we have seen thermally controlled—which terminate the arrest of growth. This dissociation is not invariable. Occasionally, when day length is the controlling agency, the growth arrest remains under the imminent control of the inducing factor.

This type of response has already been noted in *Dendrolimus* (p. 16). In this species larval growth is arrested in short days and continued in long days (Danilyevsky, 1948; Gayspitz, 1949). In *Euproctis chrysorrhoea* the growth of the larvae during the post-diapause period, and perhaps the actual release from diapause, is greatly accelerated by a photoperiod of about 20 hours (Gayspitz, 1953). And in the scelionid *Telenomus laeviusculus* dormancy is ended most expeditiously at an optimum photoperiod of 16 hours; fewer parasites undergo metamorphosis if exposed to longer or shorter day lengths (Gayspitz and Kyao, 1953). The larvae of certain treehole mosquitoes also appear to respond in a similar fashion to light (Baker, 1935).

A wide variety of stimuli, both natural and artificial, are capable of terminating diapause in *Lucilia sericata*. It has been claimed that an amelioration of the adverse conditions which have initially induced diapause may in turn lead to the resumption of growth. Favourable temperatures, the right conditions of moisture and good aeration of the culture medium have all been regarded as significant (Cousin, 1932). Diapausing larvae can also be induced to pupate merely by placing them in an empty tube. The responsible stimulus in this case seems to be the loss of contact (Mellanby, 1938). This instability may well be due to the fact that the endocrine centres which control pupation are less completely protected from 'irrelevant' sensory stimulation than in most insects. Apart from these factors, *Lucilia* is also responsive to low temperature, for dormant larvae which have been chilled at 4° C. for 26 days pupate promptly in 3 days (Roubaud, 1922). Perhaps this is the normal stimulus in nature.

THE TERMINATION OF DIAPAUSE BY CHEMICAL
AND OTHER MEANS

Various kinds of chemical, mechanical or thermal shock treatments are sometimes effective in ending diapause prematurely. *Bombyx* eggs can be reactivated by electric shocks, brushing, or immersion in warm dilute hydrochloric and sulphuric acids (Henneguy, 1904; Kogure, 1933); brief temperature shocks at 56 or 60° C. are rather less effective (Emme, 1949 *b*). The diapausing larvae of the fly *Lipara lucens* (Chloropidae) can sometimes be caused to pupate by pricking or singeing them (Varley and Butler, 1933). A variety of stimuli such as heat shocks, pricking and burns can terminate the relatively weak diapause in *Lucilia* (Roubaud, 1922). Exposure to the vapours of fat solvents such as xylol and carbon tetrachloride readily breaks the larval diapause in *Loxostege* (Pepper, 1937). The diapause eggs of *Melanoplus differentialis* when treated with xylol and supplied with water will resume development (Slifer, 1946). Nevertheless, many insects possessing an intense diapause often resist all efforts to break diapause artificially. Thus fat solvents and strong oxidizing agents have been tried without success on the pupae of the cherry fly *Rhagoletis cerasi* (Wiesmann, 1950). And wounding, even of the most severe character, does not lead to imaginal differentiation in the pupae of *Platysamia cecropia* (Schneiderman and Williams, 1953).

These agencies can be vizualized as acting in several different ways. Chemical treatment of the egg may modify the properties of the egg membranes in such a manner that the physical conditions necessary for the growth of the embryo are restored. For example, xylol treatment in *Melanoplus* permits the egg to take up the water which is a requirement for normal development. However, it is often difficult or even impossible to decide whether the chemical is acting indirectly in this way or whether it is activating the cells directly (p. 72).

When diapause occurs in the post-embryonic stages, chemical or mechanical wounding may cause increased stimulation of some centre of humoral control, such as the brain, so that the normal mechanism of control is brought into action prematurely. On the other hand, it is known that the repair of wounds in

Platysamia is associated with the local regeneration of the cyto-chrome–cytochrome oxidase system and with a greatly increased oxygen consumption. No doubt these phenomena reflect the renewal of mitotic activity in the pupal epidermis at this time. If this disturbance were propagated (as it is not in *Platysamia*), growth might be resumed without the intervention of the central endocrine mechanism.

CHAPTER 5

THE ROLE OF WATER IN THE ARREST OF GROWTH

DEFICIENCY of water is a potent factor in retarding or arresting the growth of many organisms. In some insects this quiescence is simply a function of the availability of water in the external environment. The insect becomes dormant when dehydrated but is always ready to resume growth when water is again supplied. The relationship is more complex in insects which possess a diapause. There are many species in which the absorption of water is indispensable for normal post-diapause growth; and if water is lacking, an arrest which starts as diapause may be continued as quiescence. It is not always easy to decide in these cases whether the uptake of water plays an integral part in the mechanism of diapause. Sometimes indeed the two processes appear to be entirely independent, for diapause may be found to persist even when the insect is in a fully hydrated condition. In other forms, however, there is evidence that the intake of water is more or less closely linked with the diapause state and is in abeyance so long as diapause persists. Here, seemingly, the effect of hydration on growth has been harnessed as part of the diapause mechanism.

WATER AND THE CONTROL OF EMBRYONIC GROWTH IN THE ORTHOPTERA

The absorption of water is a normal requirement of the developing orthopteran egg. The water relations may first be described in a species which lays both diapause and non-diapause eggs, namely, the South African brown locust *Locustana pardalina*. The behaviour of both types of eggs, which occur together within the same egg pod, has been very thoroughly studied by Matthée (1951). When they are provided with contact moisture during incubation, the non-diapause eggs develop without interruption and hatch in 10 days at 35° C. If they are denied water, embryonic development is slow and growth is arrested completely on the 9th day when the embryo is half-grown and almost ready to undergo revolution. In this condition the eggs possess great durability, often remaining viable for as long as 3½ years. However, if they are at any time moistened, water is immediately taken up, the egg membranes are stretched, and growth is resumed.

The behaviour of the diapause egg is entirely different. When the freshly laid eggs are moistened, the embryos develop to the pre-revolution stage and then enter diapause. At this point the eggs are turgid but have not yet taken up enough water to stretch the chorion and cuticle. If they are kept moist at 35° C. hatching eventually takes place rather irregularly after a period which may vary from 36 to 95 days. In the absence of contact water embryonic growth is comparatively slow and again ceases completely at the morphological diapause stage. The water content may then amount to about 3 mg. If the collapsed eggs are now moistened, some water is taken up—perhaps a further 3 mg.—but no more than is sufficient to restore turgor. The embryo becomes slightly broader and longer but growth is not resumed. However, when the 'dry' diapause eggs are held at 35° C. for a period of about 45 days and are then allowed contact with water, about 9 mg. are taken up, stretching the egg envelopes. The embryos then undergo revolution after the second day and hatch by the eighth.

As in other locust eggs, water is absorbed through the hydropyle, the rate of entry being controlled by the underlying hydropyle cells which form a specialized region of the serosa. Whereas the restoration of turgor may perhaps be dependent upon simple osmotic diffusion, further uptake certainly involves the active transport of water, since turgid eggs which are free of diapause can absorb water against an osmotic gradient. Although evaporation is limited by the deposition of some proteinaceous material over the hydropyle, the failure to absorb water during diapause seems to be due to the inactivity of the hydropyle cells rather than to the secretion of a waterproofing material over the hydropyle.

It is clear from these observations that in *Locustana* the entry of water is determined by the physiological condition of the egg. Eggs of the non-diapause type, or those that are free of diapause after being kept for at least 45 days at 35° C., can resume development promptly at any time. Growth is only limited by the availability of water in the external environment. On the other hand, the diapause egg will replace water lost by evaporation, but all further active absorption is in abeyance until diapause development has been completed—a process which evidently takes place with equal readiness when the egg is partially dehydrated or is in a turgid condition. Although the primary cause of the growth failure may then be ascribed to the diapause state of the egg, it still remains to be decided whether the more immediate cause of the arrest is the relatively low water content of the turgid but unswollen egg, or whether the absorption of water is merely an incidental accompaniment of the disappearance of diapause. Studies on other orthopteran eggs throw light on this problem.

The role of water in relation to diapause has been extensively studied in the egg of *Melanoplus differentialis*. The essential structures are shown in fig. 16, which is based on the researches of Slifer. The embryo and yolk of the freshly laid egg are surrounded only by the serosa, the vitelline membrane and chorion. But after 1 week of incubation the yellow and white cuticles, including the hydropylar structures at the posterior pole of the egg, are laid down by the serosa. The yellow cuticle is impermeable to water save at this point.

Although the chorion is pierced by a number of pores, the uptake of water is at first prevented by the primary wax layer which lines the chorion (Slifer, 1938, 1950). Water begins to enter the egg after the first week of incubation, while the embryo is still growing. This event coincides with the formation of the hydropylar apparatus and with the probable dissolution of the primary wax layer. During the second and third weeks nearly 1 mg. is taken up. At the end of this phase all further uptake ceases abruptly as the egg enters diapause; no water at all is admitted for an indefinite period until diapause is completed. When the egg has been chilled and is free of diapause, water uptake and embryonic growth are resumed concurrently.

2–3 mg. of water are taken in during post-diapause development, the most active phase of absorption coinciding with the early stages of catatrepsis.

The experimental and histological evidence advanced by Slifer (1938, 1946, 1948 and 1949) strongly suggests that the entry of water at the onset of diapause is cut off by the deposition of a waxy layer over the surface of the hydropyle. This barrier is itself secreted by the hydropyle cells and is also presumably broken down by them when diapause is brought to an

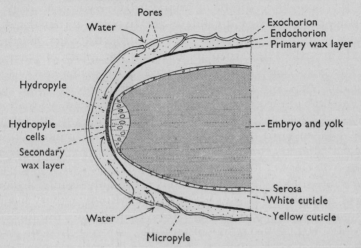

Fig. 16. Diagram showing the disposition of the extra-embryonic membranes at the posterior pole of the egg of *Melanoplus differentialis* just before the entry into diapause (after Slifer).

end by chilling. Slifer considers that the immediate cause of the growth arrest is water lack, since adequately chilled eggs will not develop if the entry of water is prevented by covering the hydropyle with an impermeable material. And diapause can be broken by immersing the egg in xylol and other wax solvents (a treatment which dissolves the waxes from the hydropyle). If the egg is then allowed to take up water in carefully controlled quantities, embryonic development is resumed.

The success of the xylol treatment in promoting healthy post-diapause growth depends upon the care exercised by the observer in controlling the entry of water: if too little is admitted the eggs will not develop; if too much, the eggs will burst. Andrewartha (1952) has pointed out that the loss of the powers of regulation must mean that the hydropyle cells have sustained an injury and that this type of 'wounding' might itself serve as a stimulus to growth. This possibility cannot easily be dismissed; indeed, some alternative explanation must be sought in the case of other diapause eggs which, although responding to xylol treatment, take up no water during the course of development. (An example is the winter egg of *Metatetranychus* (Dierick,1950).) At the same time, proof of injury to the hydropyle cells in *Melanoplus* in no way invalidates the hypothesis that the diapause state in the uninjured egg is controlled by the ability of the hydropyle cells to regulate and limit the uptake of water.

This view has been strengthened by the observations of Bucklin (1953 and personal communication) on the same egg. At the time of the growth arrest the *Melanoplus* embryo is about half-grown and lies at the surface of the yolk (fig. 17). If embryo and yolk, enclosed by the serosal membrane, are removed from the cuticular envelopes and are suspended in a hanging drop of Ringer's solution, diapause is immediately brought to an end. The embryonic cells, at first cloudy, gradually assume a more glassy appearance as water is imbibed. Mitotic activity begins within a few hours. The embryos even undergo 'revolution', creeping round the surface of the yolk, just as if the yolk were still enclosed by the shell. In due course the yolk is drawn in as dorsal closure is effected; peristaltic contractions commence, and sometimes the embryos undergo the intermediate moult which usually occurs after hatching.

Whole embryos cultured in this manner tolerate considerable variations of osmotic pressure; development continues in Ringer of either half or double the normal isosmotic concentration. Neither is the ionic composition critical, for the embryo will also undergo revolution in isosmotic sodium chloride. Solutions of potassium chloride and non-electrolytes such as mannitol are highly toxic so that many pyknotic nuclei are found and revolution fails. However, there are still some mitotic figures, indicating that diapause is ended in these media. Bucklin has therefore concluded that the free access to water is the significant attribute of the new environment.

The Role of Water in the Arrest of Growth

Water absorption and diapause occupy entirely different positions in the programme of development of other orthopteran eggs. These time relations are summarized in fig. 17. In *Austroicetes* the water content of the turgid egg rises steadily throughout anatrepsis when the embryo is in diapause although developing slowly. By the time the egg is free of diapause and the embryo about to undergo revolution, nearly 40 % of the total water uptake has been completed. Alternate desiccation and rehydration is without influence on the termination of diapause, just as in the *Locustana* egg (Birch and Andrewartha, 1942). The general pattern of water absorption is probably very similar in the eggs of *Dociostaurus maroccanus* (Bodenheimer and

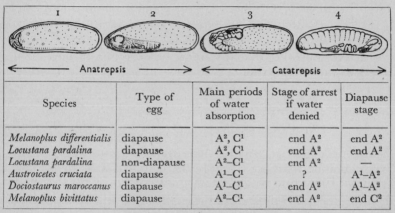

Species	Type of egg	Main periods of water absorption	Stage of arrest if water denied	Diapause stage
Melanoplus differentialis	diapause	A^2, C^1	end A^2	end A^2
Locustana pardalina	diapause	A^2, C^1	end A^2	end A^2
Locustana pardalina	non-diapause	A^2–C^1	end A^2	—
Austroicetes cruciata	diapause	A^1–C^1	?	A^1–A^2
Dociostaurus maroccanus	diapause	A^1–C^1	end A^2	A^1–A^2
Melanoplus bivittatus	diapause	A^2–C^1	end A^2	end C^2

Fig. 17. Water uptake and water lack in relation to embryonic development in certain grasshoppers and locusts. The symbols A^1, A^2, C^1, C^2 refer to the first and second halves of anatrepsis and catatrepsis respectively. The figure shows four stages in the embryogenesis of *Melanoplus differentialis* (after Burkholder). 1, appearance of germ band (5th day); 2, diapause stage at end of anatrepsis (21st day); 3, embryo revolving round posterior pole after termination of diapause; 4, embryo at close of catatrepsis after fusion of dorsal line and lateral rotation.

Shulov, 1951). Although these species differ from *Locustana* and *Melanoplus differentialis* in absorbing some water during diapause, uptake is most active in the early post-diapause period as growth is resumed. The extent of the hydration at the end of anatrepsis might therefore still be insufficient to permit active embryonic growth.

However, this interpretation cannot be applied in other cases where the absorption of water is almost complete before the egg

73

enters diapause. In the egg of *M. bivittatus* 88 % of the total water uptake has occurred by the end of anatrepsis. Yet diapause does not supervene until the end of catatrepsis when the nymph is within a few days of hatching (Salt, 1949 *a*, *b*, 1952). *Gryllulus commodus* is a second species in which it is difficult to associate the arrest of growth with the water content of the egg. If the freshly laid eggs of this cricket are chilled for an adequate period, diapause development is completed before the embryo has grown to the morphological diapause stage (p. 61). All the water required for healthy post-diapause growth, equal to twice the original weight of the egg, is taken in subsequently. But when the eggs are incubated under moist conditions at a temperature of 25° C., almost all the water is imbibed in the first 3 or 4 days so that the egg enters diapause in a fully hydrated condition (Browning, 1953). It seems then that in these species the active control of diapause must be exercised through some agency other than water.

THE PROLONGATION OF DORMANCY BY WATER
LACK IN LARVAL AND ADULT INSECTS

Many insect larvae which enter diapause with an increased proportion of dry matter restore the water balance in the post-diapause period by imbibing moisture from their surroundings. If these insects are denied contact with water, the resumption of growth may be delayed or even prevented indefinitely. However, their condition is now one of quiescence for they are soon reactivated if water is supplied. Because of this effect water has often been mistaken for the agency which terminates diapause.

The absorption of water is sometimes more or less closely associated with the physiological condition of the larva. In the borer *Chilo simplex*, the pupation of larvae which have hibernated outdoors in Japan is delayed by a month or more if the rice stems containing the insects are kept dry. The dehydrated larvae readily take up water and pupate if the straw is moistened in May or June, but no water is absorbed in December while the larvae are still firmly in diapause (Koidsumi, 1952). Most of the water enters through the mouth, although a little is admitted through the cuticle. Absorption at both sites seems to become greater as diapause development nears completion (Koidsumi and Makino, 1953). Babcock's older work (1927*a*) suggests that the water relations are similar in *Pyrausta nubilalis*.

According to Townsend (1926), hibernating larvae of the codling moth may be induced to pupate by immersing them in water. However, this result has not been confirmed by Theron (1943) or Andrewartha (1952) who were unable to induce pupation by this means, even if the larvae were forced to take up water by abrading them with alumina dust. If the uptake of water is of normal occurrence in *Cydia*, it would seem likely that this takes place after diapause development has been completed at low temperature. Evidently this process is not hastened if water absorption is induced prematurely.

TABLE 5. *Water uptake in* Cephus cinctus *in relation to the completion of diapause development at low temperature* (*from Church*)

Duration of chilling at 10° C. (days)	Ratio of water to dry matter: larvae chilled in moist soil	Larvae developing in moist soil at 30° C. after chilling in	
		Dry soil	Moist soil
0	1·22	0	0
50	1·43	83	84
75	1·41	97	99
100	1·52	92	100
Prepupae	1·64	—	—

Lack of moisture will sometimes prevent the resumption of growth in the wheat stem sawfly *Cephus cinctus*. But the pattern of water absorption, which has been carefully followed by Church (1953), bears little relation to the progress of diapause development. Diapause in this species is obligatory and sets in after the mature larva has partly cut through the stem and has lined the tunnel in the wheat stub with a cocoon. The arrest is terminated in about 100 days at 10° C. (Salt, 1947). When larvae are chilled at this temperature under moist conditions the ratio of water to dry matter increases throughout the period of diapause development, this trend being continued in the prepupa (table 5). If the larvae are chilled in dry soil and are only permitted to imbibe water during subsequent incubation at a higher temperature, diapause development is not retarded.

Evidently the two processes are quite unconnected in this species.

Access to free water during the post-diapause period is also important in many other insects. The pupation of the over-wintering larvae of the tortricid *Epiblema strenuana*, and the emergence of their parasites, is considerably delayed if water is withheld in spring (Rice, 1937). The 'resting' larvae of the subtropical crambid *Diatraea lineolata* have been observed to pupate when the dry corn stalks in which they are tunnelling become wetted by rain (Kevan, 1944). High humidities and contact with water also facilitate pupation in long-dormant larvae of the bollworm *Platyedra* (Squire, 1940). Overwintering box-elder bugs (*Leptocoris trivittatus*) remain inactive until their water balance has been restored in spring (Hodson, 1937). Hibernating Mexican bean beetles (*Epilachna corrupta*) tend to leave the soil during the first warm days of spring. But as the resumption of activity is delayed by any lack of moisture in the soil, the emergence peaks usually coincide closely with the periods of rainfall (Douglass, 1928, 1933).

The mechanisms by which this restraint is exercised have not yet been studied. However, it is known that in *Cephus* and other larvae the resumption of growth is controlled by the brain and prothoracic glands, while in adult insects there is reason to associate the development of the reproductive organs during the post-diapause period with the activity of the corpus allatum (see Chapter 8). Dehydration may influence the epidermis directly, but it seems more probable that it inhibits the liberation of one or other of the hormones required for growth or reproduction.

THE ARREST OF GROWTH BY PARTIAL DEHYDRATION

There are many other arthropods, often lacking a definitive diapause, which become quiescent if their water content falls below a certain critical level. Their resting stages often combine considerable resistance to desiccation with a wide tolerance of water loss; however, they are killed if desiccation proceeds too far.

The eggs of locusts have been mentioned earlier. The non-diapause eggs of *Locustana* will survive a fall in moisture content from about 85 to 40 %. In their natural habitat, the Karroo desert, the eggs may lie dormant for several years. The very slight but well-distributed rainfall of this area is particularly favourable for lengthy survival, since the soil may from time to time contain sufficient moisture for the egg to recover turgor. But growth cannot be resumed until the soil is thoroughly wetted by a heavy fall of rain (Matthée, 1951).

The red-legged earth mite *Halotydeus destructor* (Penthaleidae), an important pasture pest in Western Australia, possesses eggs of two types. The 'winter' eggs are laid on vegetation and are readily killed by desiccation. The 'aestivating' eggs are retained in the body of the female mite after death. Within this additional protective envelope of cuticle they prove exceedingly resistant, remaining viable for over 4 years in dry soil. The eggs shrivel but do not apparently lose all their water content. When moistened they take up water and burst, releasing the 'deutovum' from which the larva soon emerges (Norris, 1950). The eggs of *Sminthurus viridis* (Collembola) appear to possess similar properties (Holdaway, 1927; Davidson, 1932).

The eggs of mosquitoes of the genus *Aëdes*, which are commonly laid on soil and other moist surfaces, sometimes become dormant when the embryo is fully formed and apparently ready to hatch. In this state they can withstand considerable desiccation. Besides the imbibition of water, an additional stimulus is required for hatching, namely, a low oxygen tension. These conditions can be reproduced experimentally by the addition to the medium of mild reducing agents such as glutathione or cysteine. The presence of organic plant debris or the growth of bacteria in the medium will provoke hatching in *A. vexans* and *A. lateralis* for the same reason (Gjullin, Hegarty and Bollen, 1941). The turgid eggs of *A. aegypti* may even be induced to hatch in air if oxygen is removed with an alkaline solution pyrogallol (Geigy and Gander, 1949; Gander, 1951).

The presence of contact water is indispensable for the prompt development of several species of gall midges. In the case of the hessian fly, *Mayetiola destructor*, ecological observations in France have shown that development is uninterrupted in the more humid climate of the Vendée. But in the low rainfall area of the Midi the first generation aestivate in the pupal stage, the appearance of the second generation adults then being delayed until the autumn (Marchal, 1897). In this instance, however, abundant moisture may not be the only requirement. The fact that development often fails at temperatures above 20° C., regardless of the humidity conditions, is suggestive of a diapause mechanism (Zhukovsky, 1950). The multivoltine cecidomyiid *Schizomyia macarangae* breeds continuously in southern India except during the dry summer months of March–June. The galls, which are formed by the larvae in the leaves of the macaranga tree, break away and fall to the ground when ripe. The mature larvae will remain quiescent for as long as 8 months if kept dry in the laboratory but can be induced to pupate at any time by wetting the galls (Nayar, 1953). Low atmospheric humidity may also be the agency responsible for the dry-season quiescence of the sorghum midge *Contarinia sorghicola* in East Africa (Geering, 1953).

Summer torpor in *Syrphus ribesii* is certainly due to desiccation; when the larvae are moistened water is taken up through the anal papilli and growth is resumed (Schneider, 1948). The larval development of the twig-cutting weevil *Rhynchites coeruleus* is delayed by many months if the fallen shoots in which the grubs are mining are protected from the rain (Guennelon-Aubanel, 1951). The 'ground pearl' *Margarodes vitium* is noted for the longevity of the nymphs which form hard wax-coated cysts on the roots of the vine. Mayet (1896) was able to revive nymphs which had been dormant for 7 years by immersing them in water. One specimen of this coccid examined by Ferris (1919) remained alive after storage for 17 years in a museum.

THE ARREST OF GROWTH BY TOTAL DEHYDRATION

A few animals, mainly those inhabiting small impermanent bodies of water, have evolved no protective devices for preventing the evaporation of water but are able to withstand complete dehydration without injury. This property, which is found in some Protozoa, rotifers and tardigrades, is shared by a small number of arthropods. The larva of the mycetophilid *Sciara medullaris* described by Giard (1902) may belong to this group. However, a better known example is provided by the larva of *Polypedilum vanderplanki* which has been studied in detail by Hinton (1951, 1953a). This chironomid breeds in shallow temporary rock pools in northern Nigeria. When these dry out, the larvae soon become dehydrated and shrivel to almost unrecognizable proportions (fig. 18). Specimens in this condition have remained viable for over 3 years. If they are replaced in water the larvae rapidly imbibe water and swim away within an hour or so. They can be desiccated and reactivated repeatedly. 'Dry' larvae usually contain about 15% of hygroscopic moisture, but the water content can be reduced to 1% or less without affecting the recovery in water.

The physiology of the dormant larvae is remarkable in other ways. No respiration has yet been detected. Dried larvae

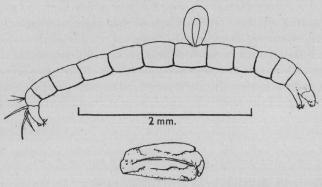

Fig. 18. *Polypedilum vanderplanki* (after Hinton). Larva dried for over 3 years and the same twenty minutes after immersion in water. This particular larva had the tergite of the third abdominal segment torn open during the years it was dry. A section of the gut was forced through the tear when it absorbed water, and the larva ceased to move and eventually died about 4 hours afterwards.

survive exposure to a temperature of 65° C. for 20 hours, whereas the limit of tolerance in the active larva is about 41° C. Resistance to high temperatures probably depends upon the removal of all traces of water from the tissues. The eggs of the brine shrimp *Artemia salina*, which possess similar properties, will hatch after exposure to a temperature of 103° C. for 4 hours provided they are first carefully dried. Dehydrated *Polypedilum* larvae will also tolerate injuries that prove rapidly fatal when they are reactivated (fig. 18). Many of these properties reflect the possession of some effective intracellular mechanism for preventing protein denaturation.

CHAPTER 6

DIAPAUSE AND QUIESCENCE IN PARASITIC INSECTS

———

THE life cycles of many insect parasitoids and their hosts are very precisely synchronized. This close linkage is often due to the fact that the rhythm of development is determined by the host. In an association of this type the growth of the parasite is delayed if the host enters diapause but is uninterrupted if the latter develops without arrest (Salt, 1941). There are, however, other relationships in which the parasite appears as the active partner. And it is also necessary to consider the possibility that an intimate adjustment can be achieved by host and parasite both responding to the same 'token' stimulus in the environment.

THE INFLUENCE OF THE HOST ON THE GROWTH OF THE PARASITE

Synchronous development is most striking when the host possesses a facultative diapause or when the parasite can develop in two species that differ in voltinism. An example is afforded by the braconid egg parasite *Chelonus annulipes* which attacks either the single- or multiple-brooded strains of the cornborer *Pyrausta nubilalis* (Bradley and Arbuthnot, 1938). The development of the parasite in the first generation of the bivoltine race is completed in 2 months, and the emergent adults are then ready to parasitize the eggs of the second annual generation of cornborers. However, in these hosts, which are destined to enter diapause in autumn as mature larvae, the active growth of the parasite is deferred until the following spring, when the *Pyrausta* pupates. The life cycle of the parasite therefore occupies 10 months in this host or 1 year if the *Chelonus* has invaded the eggs of the univoltine strain.

The restraint exercised by the host is even more remarkable

in the wheat-blossom midge *Sitodiplosis mosellana*. Although the majority of parasites (and unparasitized hosts) emerge after only one winter below ground, soil containing diapause larvae has yielded hymenopterous parasites 7 years after their hosts have ceased feeding. The general correspondence between the annual emergences of hosts and parasites suggests that the development of the latter is contingent upon the pupation of *Sitodiplosis*. But the arrest is on the whole rather less prolonged than in the host which may overwinter 12 times (Barnes, 1943, 1952).

This conformity is achieved in the following manner. Many hymenopterous and tachinid parasitoids possess a specialized stage, often the 1st-instar larva, which lies dormant until activated by some specific physiological event in the life history of the host. The required stimulus may be supplied during the post-diapause growth of the egg, by pupation or imaginal differentiation or by the maturation of the ovaries of the host. Provided the event in question comes *after* the growth arrest in the host has been terminated, the pattern of development as a whole will be set by the diapause of the host. It will be noted that it is not the occurrence of development *per se* which is the activating stimulus.

In *Scelio chortoicetes*, an egg parasite of the Australian grasshopper *Austroicetes*, the necessary stimulus is provided during later stages of development of the host egg. The freshly laid eggs of the grasshopper are attacked in November at the beginning of the southern summer. During the 9 months diapause period the parasite remains quiescent as a 1st-instar larva. The phase of active growth is confined to 2 or 3 months after dormancy in the *Austroicetes* egg is ended. The life cycle, lasting 1 year, therefore remains exactly attuned to that of the host (Birch, 1945).

The 1st-instar larva is also the dormant stage in *Chelonus*. As we have seen, the resumption of growth is initiated by the pupation of the host, *Pyrausta*. In this instance the parasite is evidently unresponsive to the larval moults of the host. The zygaenid *Harrisina brillians*, which enters diapause as a pupa, is often infested by an unidentified species of *Sturmia*. This tachinid overwinters in exactly the same manner, namely, as a quiescent 1st-instar larva within the host pupa (Smith and

Langston, 1953). In this case, however, the parasite is clearly unaffected by the pupation of the host, yet it is activated as the host undergoes metamorphosis the following spring.

In the encyrtid *Diversinervus smithi*, which oviposits in the large fused ganglion of the young scale *Saissetia oleae*, the stimulus seems to be associated with the maturation of the host's ovaries. The young larvae remain immobile until the host is fully developed and the ovaries distended with ripe eggs. Then the parasite breaks out into the body cavity, moults and rapidly completes its development (Flanders, 1939, 1944).

MECHANISM OF THE RESPONSE TO THE HOST

The ichneumonid *Diplazon fissorius* has recently been used by Schneider (1950, 1951) for studying the type of restraint which is exercised by the host. The eggs are deposited in young syrphid larvae, but although they soon hatch, the 1st-instar parasites undergo no further development until the host pupates. In *Epistrophe balteata*, a multivoltine syrphid which hibernates as an adult, this delay is only a matter of a few days. When the species attacked is *Syphus ribesii*, which usually aestivates for some weeks, the duration of the host's quiescence is exactly matched by the delay in the activation of the parasite. A third syrphid, the univoltine *Epistrophe bifasciata*, has a prolonged larval diapause, often enduring for 9 months. In this host the parasite overwinters as a young larva and only resumes its development in spring when the host forms the puparium. In this way the life cycles of parasite and host remain synchronized whether the latter is uni- or multivoltine.

Although no food is ingested through the mouth, the quiescent 1st-instar larvae of *Diplazon fissorius* actively absorbs amino acids through the permeable hydrophilic cuticle and eventually builds up considerable reserves of protein. When stimulated by the pupation of the host, the larva moves forward to the vicinity of the brain and principal imaginal disks, discharges a copious flow of saliva and fills the alimentary canal with blood. The toxic properties of the saliva prevent the pupal moult and also inhibit the growth of the imaginal disks, injuring and eventually destroying them. After a rapid succession of moults, the histolysis of the pupal contents is completed by the 5th-instar parasite larva.

Schneider was able to prove conclusively that the activity of the young *Diplazon* larvae was directly controlled by the properties of the blood of the host. If young larvae, newly activated by the pupation of their host (*Epistrophe balteata*), are injected into diapausing larvae of *E. bifasciata*, they are immediately immobilized. Conversely, dormant larvae are instantly activated when they are transferred to the body cavity of a pupating *E. balteata*. These experiments show that in this instance the arrest can more appropriately be regarded as 'quiescence'.

Schneider attributes the immobilization of the young parasite larvae to the presence in the blood of some inhibitory substance which disappears at pupation. It is perhaps equally probable that the arrest of growth is caused by the lack of a growth-promoting factor. Indeed, it is even possible that the parasite is responding to the same humoral changes that regulate pupation in the host. Thus quiescent larvae of *Diplazon fissorius* also become activated in the presence of a second species, *D. pectoratorius*, the larvae of which are known to secrete a substance mimicking the action of the 'pupation hormone' (see p. 86).

INDEPENDENT RESPONSE OF PARASITE AND HOST TO THE ENVIRONMENT

Many hymenopterous parasites exhibit two entirely different forms of arrest, quiescence during an early larval instar and a definitive diapause at the close of the last larval stage. *Opius melleus*, a parasite of the apple maggot *Rhagoletis*, and the braconids *Alysia manducator* and *Aphaereta minuta*, have this faculty (Lathrop and Newton, 1933; Evans, 1933). In these instances the early larval arrests are probably governed by the development of the host. But it is doubtful whether the impending diapause condition of the host can be communicated to the parasite after the host itself has been consumed. Evidence to the contrary has recently been secured in the case of the braconid *Apanteles glomeratus*.

When *Apanteles* develops in the larvae of *Pieris brassicae*—an insect with a facultative pupal diapause—the fully grown parasite larvae leave the host as it prepares to pupate and after spinning a cluster of cocoons proceed to hibernate as prepupae. The univoltine pierid *Aporia crataegi*, which enters diapause as a 2nd- or 3rd-instar larva, is also sometimes attacked. In this environment, however, the *Apanteles* overwinter as young larvae within the host (Faure, 1926, cited in Salt, 1941). There is no doubt therefore that the growth of the parasite is delayed until the larval development of the host is far advanced.

But in addition to this early arrest, *Apanteles* displays a true facultative diapause in the prepupal stage. Gayspitz and Kyao (1953), who have examined the relationship of *Apanteles* with *Pieris*, have shown that the host and parasite respond quite independently to the external environment, the length of day being of particular importance. Parasite and host are both 'long-day' insects so that their diapause is prevented in long days and induced in short days. But the independence of the response is revealed by a slight disparity in the critical photoperiods. When infested hosts are reared with a photoperiod of 16 hours 45 minutes only 25 % of the emerging parasites enter diapause, whereas the incidence of diapause among unparasitized hosts reaches 93 %. This difference is probably too trivial to deprive the parasites of a significant number of hosts in the next generation. Although *Apanteles* is responsive to photoperiod while still endoparasitic, it remains sensitive for some time after leaving the host. The parasite can therefore be prevented from entering diapause by exposure to a long photoperiod immediately after emergence from the host, even though the latter has previously been determined for diapause by rearing in short days.

It may well be that Marchal's (1936) experiments with *Trichogramma cacaeciae* should be interpreted along similar lines. The life cycle of this egg parasite in the univoltine tortricid *Cacoecia rosana* has been summarized by Salt in diagrammatic form (fig. 19). It will be observed that there are two generations of *Trichogramma* to each one of *Cacoecia*. The macropterous females of the summer generation attack the host egg masses soon after they are laid in July. After quickly consuming the contents of the egg, the mature larvae enter a diapause which persists for some 7 months. The females which emerge in March are micropterous, and these individuals proceed to oviposit in

84

the unparasitized and still unhatched outer eggs in the cluster. Their progeny complete their development in about 7 weeks, becoming the macropterous females of the summer generation.

Since the host eggs are in diapause by July and are free of diapause by March, the slow and rapid generations appeared to be associated with these conditions. In other experiments by Marchal the *Trichogramma* was reared in the eggs of the cabbage moth *Mamestra brassicae*, a species with a pupal diapause. In

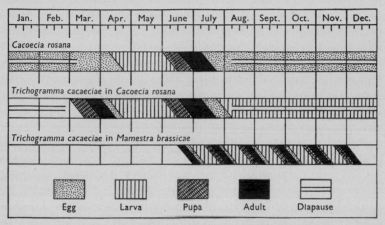

Fig. 19. The life cycle of the parasite *Trichogramma cacaeciae* when developing in the eggs of a univoltine host, *Cacoecia rosana*, and in those of a multivoltine host, *Mamestra brassicae* (from Salt, after Marchal).

these eggs the parasites always developed promptly, seven or more generations being completed during the summer and autumn (fig. 19). Nevertheless, the active development of the host egg was not required, for freshly laid eggs killed in a moist heat also furnished the appropriate environment for rapid development.

Several writers have concluded that these observations provide strong evidence for the existence of a persistent 'diapause substance' in the host egg which, after ingestion, exerts a like inhibitory effect upon the development of the parasite. However, the assumption that some general seasonal factor, such as the length of day, is acting differentially upon the parasite in spring and summer would provide an equally consistent explanation of the life cycle in *Cacoecia*. The crucial evidence relates to the behaviour of *Trichogramma* in *Mamestra*. But as the conditions of photoperiod and temperature were not defined, the implications of this experiment remain uncertain.

THE INFLUENCE OF THE PARASITE ON
THE DIAPAUSING HOST

It is well known that several species of Diptera, which normally hibernate in the last larval instar, form their puparia prematurely in autumn if they have been invaded by hymenopterous parasites. The apparent ability of the parasite to terminate diapause in the host could be ascribed to several possible causes. The wound inflicted by the adult parasite has been regarded as a probable stimulus. Then again, the parasite larva could be visualized as activating the humoral centres of the host or, alternatively, as influencing the tissues directly without the intervention of these centres. Observations by Varley and Butler (1933) on the chloropid fly *Lipara lucens*, which pupates prematurely when attacked by the braconid *Polemon liparae*, militate against the first possibility. Although the arrest of growth in *Lipara* could sometimes be ended by singeing or pricking the larvae, the numbers pupating were not so large as to suggest that the oviposition puncture of the parasite could be the sole causative agency.

This view has been confirmed by Schneider's (1950, 1951) experiments with *Diplazon pectoratorius*. The relationships of this ichneumonid with the syrphid *Epistrophe bifasciata* differ entirely from those of its congener *Diplazon fissorius*. *D. pectoratorius* begins to feed immediately after hatching from the egg but exerts little effect upon the host until the latter has been in diapause for about 1 month. The cooler conditions of autumn then seem to activate the parasite larva which moults and secretes saliva. The moulting hormone discharged by the parasite appears to diffuse through the body wall, causing the host to form the puparium. Meanwhile, the saliva prevents the ring gland from functioning and blocks the growth of the brain and imaginal anlage. After the induced pupation of the host, the *Diplazon* histolyses the contents of the puparium and itself enters diapause as a mature 5th-instar larva.

86

Diapause and Quiescence in Parasitic Insects

When larvae of *D. pectoratorius* are injected into the posterior compartment of a transversely ligatured diapausing *Epistrophe* larva, this fragment forms a puparium while the anterior half remains larval. The pupation of the host is not therefore induced by the activation of its own endocrine centres following an injury stimulus, but by the direct action of the parasite on the epidermis of the host. The induced pupation which has been observed in *Lucilia sericata* (Holdaway and Evans, 1930; Davies, 1930; Salt, 1932) and other species may well be due to a similar loss of humoral autonomy.

CHAPTER 7

METABOLIC ADJUSTMENT IN THE DORMANT INSECT

It is generally accepted that the energy requirements for growth are substantially greater than the requirements for tissue maintenance. As Williams (1948) has emphasized, the faculty of segregating these processes is one of the distinctive characteristics of the insect with diapause. The substitution of this diapause metabolism permits the economical utilization of the food reserves and thus ensures lengthy survival. The quantitative changes in metabolism and the mechanisms of adjustment are examined in this chapter.

THE ACCUMULATION OF RESERVES DURING THE PREDIAPAUSE PERIOD

Prior to their entry into diapause many insects feed ravenously and build up large reserves of fat and glycogen in the fat body and other storage tissues. This process is usually accompanied by a steady decline in the ratio of water to dry matter. For example, in the codling moth *Cydia pomonella* the fat content of the larva rises from 11 % in June to 18 % of the dry weight at the inception of diapause in August; concurrently, the water content falls from 72 to 58 % (Ushatinskaya, 1952). The hypertrophy of the fat body is particularly evident in many insects with an imaginal diapause. Thus fat may form up to 56 % of the dry weight in the cold-hardy noctuid *Scoliopterix libatrix* (Sacharov, 1930) and up to 60 % in hibernating females of *Culex pipiens* (Buxton, 1935). In *Gastrophilus* both fat and glycogen are stored abundantly in the cells of the tracheal organ (Levenbook, 1951 *a*).

The few comparative observations on species possessing a facultative arrest suggest that insects lay down more abundant

88

reserves if they are destined for diapause. In the dormant larva of *Platyedra* 43 % of the dry weight is due to fat, in the developing larva only 28 % (Squire, 1940). An excess of dry matter has also been recorded in the diapausing larvae of *Lucilia* (Mellanby, 1938).

THE LEVEL OF ACTIVITY IN THE DORMANT INSECT

Most larval and adult insects show some degree of torpor once diapause has set in. Although capable of weak movements when extracted from the egg, the fully formed larvae of *Timarcha tenebricosa* (Chrysomelidae) will not bite their way through the shell until diapause is terminated by cold (Abeloos, 1935), Third-instar larvae of the syrphid *Epistrophe bifasciata* become progressively less sensitive to tactile stimulation as diapause approaches, while the contractions of the heart decline in frequency and finally cease altogether (Schneider, 1948). The mosquito *Anopheles maculipennis messeae* remains completely immobile from November to March and cannot be aroused either by sensory stimulation or by a rise in temperature. Females of the races *typicus* and *atroparvus* select warmer hibernation quarters and are intermittently active. Nevertheless, the occasional blood meals are used for replenishing the fat body and not for developing the ovaries (Guelmino, 1951).

It is noteworthy, however, that in a few insects which hibernate as adults, the inception of diapause is marked by intense migratory activity. The pentatomid *Eurygaster integriceps* passes through a preparatory feeding period when the thoracic musculature, fat body and stink glands become enlarged and the crop is filled with food. In Turkestan the pentatomids leave the cereal fields in June and fly from the valleys to aestivation sites in the mountains (Fedotov, 1944). The moth *Agrotis infusa*, which assembles in vast numbers in the mountains of south-east Australia, is a further example. At the time of their migratory flight from the plains the moths possess immature ovaries and well-developed fat bodies (Common, 1952).

THE RATE OF RESPIRATION

The arrest of growth (and the decline in locomotory and feeding activity which accompanies the onset of diapause in larval and adult insects) is invariably associated with a striking fall in the level of metabolism. In the egg of *Melanoplus differentialis* the oxygen consumption increases from 0·1 to nearly 0·4 cu.mm. per hour during the first 3 weeks of incubation. From this point, when the half-grown embryo enters diapause, the rate of uptake

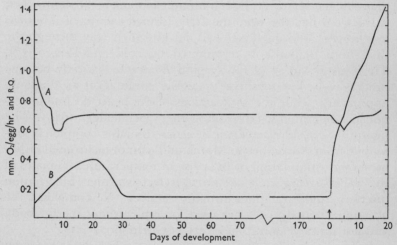

Fig. 20. A, respiratory quotient and B, oxygen consumption of the egg of *Melanoplus differentialis* during embryonic development (after Boell). Pre-diapause period from 0 to 20 days; diapause from 21 days to arrow; post-diapause period from arrow to 19 days.

falls off to about 0·17 cu.mm., a level which is maintained, almost without change, throughout the 100 or so days of dormancy. As growth is resumed, the rate of consumption rises steadily until the larva hatches (fig. 20B) (Bodine, 1929; Boell, 1935). The intensity of respiration is always closely linked to growth. Thus in *Bombyx*, which enters diapause as an unsegmented embryo, the decline in oxygen uptake comes after the first day of incubation (Ashbel, 1930, 1932), whereas in *Lymantria dispar* uptake only falls off after the 19th day when the embryo has grown to the diapause stage—in this case the fully developed but unhatched larva (Tuleschkov, 1935).

Metabolic Adjustment in the Dormant Insect

A similar relationship has also been described in many insect larvae (Kozhantshikov, 1938 a; Bodine and Evans, 1932). When the arrest occurs in the pupal stage the falling curve of oxygen consumption associated with pupation is masked by the larger decline which accompanies the entry into diapause. Nevertheless, these differences can still be detected in species such as *Deilephila euphorbiae* which possess a facultative diapause (Heller, 1926). Forty days after the inception of diapause the oxygen uptake of this insect has fallen from 240 to about 22 cu.mm. per g. per hour. However, this 'maintenance' oxygen consumption is less than half the minimum level in the non-diapause pupa.

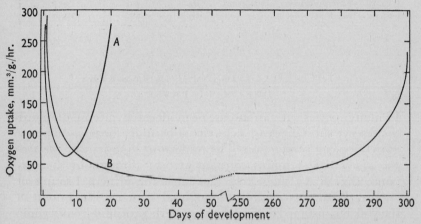

Fig. 21. Oxygen consumption of *Deilephila euphorbiae* during pupal development (after Heller). A, non-diapause pupa; B, diapause pupa.

The respiration in the latter follows the U-shaped curve typical of pupal development generally (fig. 21 A, B). Comparable results have been secured with the diapause pupae of *Platysamia cecropia* (Schneiderman and Williams, 1953).

Seasonal metabolic changes in an insect hibernating as an adult are illustrated in table 6. In the tenebrionid *Anatolica eremita* the oxygen consumption declines progressively after September, when the beetle ceases to feed, and reaches a low point in January. Although hibernation is not ended until April, the rising curve of oxygen consumption probably indicates the true point of termination of diapause (Edelman, 1951).

TABLE 6. *Trends in the water and fat content and in the oxygen consumption of the beetle* Anatolica eremita *during hibernation (from Edelman)*

Date	Condition of beetles	% water	Fat, % dry wt.	Oxygen uptake (cu.mm./g./hr.)
29. ix	Active and feeding	60	12·0	523
25. x	Hibernating	56	12·9	276
25. xi	Hibernating	53	11·0	197
25. i	Hibernating	53	7·8	115
25. ii	Hibernating	56	6·6	192
25. iii	Hibernating	60	5·8	437
10. iv	Emerging from hibernation	62	4·0	937
25. iv	Feeding	63	5·5	1236

THE UTILIZATION OF THE RESERVES
DURING DIAPAUSE

In many species with an intense or moderately intense diapause the reserve substances are kept virtually intact for post-diapause growth or egg production. The respiratory quotient in *Melano-plus differentialis* remains constant at 0·71 throughout the diapause (fig. 20A), suggesting that fat is the principal source of energy (Boell, 1935). But although 50 % of the fat content of the yolk is consumed during the 40 or so days of active embryonic growth, no depletion during the 3 or 4 months diapause period can be detected (Slifer, 1930). In the diapausing prepupae of *Gilpinia polytoma* less than 2 % of the energy stores are mobilized during the winter period. The adult sawfly does not feed; but even if the prepupa overwinters four or five times the fecundity is very little affected (Prebble, 1941 d). The reduction in the fat content of hibernating *Ephestia elutella* and *Leptinotarsa* is also comparatively slight (Waloff, 1949; Busnel and Drilhon, 1937).

In some insects, however, the rate of consumption of the reserves is more substantial. In the beetle *Anatolica eremita* the fat content falls from 12 % of the dry weight in September, when feeding ceases, to 4 % in April when feeding activity is again resumed (table 6) (Edelman, 1951). Female *Culex pipiens* also emerge from diapause in March in an emaciated condition,

92

having exhausted two-thirds of the stored fat during the hibernation period (Buxton, 1935).

Evidence that the basal level of metabolism during diapause is a highly variable feature is provided by the differing rates of weight loss in certain lepidopterous pupae (Danilyevsky, 1951). The fall in weight over a 7 months period at a humidity of 70–80 % R.H. is 3–6 times more rapid in *Smerinthus ocellatus* than in the smaller pupae of *Phalera bucephala*. These differences seem mainly to be a reflexion of the rate of mobilization of the reserves. Low rates of mobilization are associated with an intense diapause. In *Phalera*, for example, the arrest may persist for 2 or 3 years, whereas in *Smerinthus* survival for more than 1 year is rare.

Extremely low respiratory quotients have often been recorded in dormant insects. In *Formica ulkei* the mean respiratory quotient for the active and hibernating ant has been given as 0·87 and 0·5 respectively (Dreyer, 1932). And in his studies of the pupal metabolism of *Phalera* Agrell (1951 *a*) obtained respiratory quotients as low as 0·35. These values have been attributed either to the incomplete combustion of fat or to the conversion of an oxygen-poor into an oxygen-rich substrate—perhaps fat and carbohydrate respectively. However, the observations of Punt (1950) and Schneiderman and Williams (1953) have shown that although oxygen is taken up continuously, the evolution of carbon dioxide is intermittent. In *Platysamia* 90 % of the carbon dioxide is accumulated within the pupa and is released in 'bursts' which occur only once in 8 hours at 25° C. These authors point out that this is a likely source of error unless estimations extend over a relatively long period of time. After due allowance has been made for the periodic evolution of CO_2 in *Platysamia*, the respiratory quotient has been found to be 0·78, a value consistent with the combustion of a mixture of fat and carbohydrate.

MECHANISMS OF CELLULAR RESPIRATION IN RELATION TO GROWTH AND DIAPAUSE

The failure of growth, as we have seen, is closely linked with a fall in the respiration rate. It is now known that this quantitative change is mediated by qualitative adjustments in the

93

intracellular enzyme systems which control oxidative metabolism. Attention has been focused principally upon the nature of the terminal oxidase in growing and diapausing insects. In this respect the cytochrome system of Warburg–Keilin occupies a central position. The pigments of this series are all conjugated proteins with an iron-containing prosthetic group allied to haem. The components which are significant in the present context include cytochrome oxidase which catalyses the aerobic oxidation of cytochrome c, and members of the b group which are slowly oxidized by molecular oxygen without the intervention of cytochrome oxidase. Respiratory poisons such as carbon monoxide and cyanide form complexes with heavy metals and, by combining with cytochrome oxidase, prevent the oxidation of reduced cytochrome c. The iron-CO compound is dissociated by light.

Following the earlier observations by Runnström (1930) on the cyanide insensitivity of the unfertilized sea-urchin egg, these methods were applied by Bodine (1934) to the egg of *Melanoplus differentialis*. The respiration of the diapausing egg of this grasshopper also proved to be of this cyanide-stable type. Only 20 % of the diapause respiration is abolished by 0·001 M cyanide, whereas 70–80 % of the respiration of the actively growing post-diapause embryo is reversibly inhibited at this concentration. The extent of the inhibition is at first roughly proportional to the size of the embryo and to the oxygen uptake (fig. 22 B, C). The fall in respiration after cyanide poisoning is therefore negligible during the first few days of incubation, but increases steadily as cytochrome oxidase is synthesized (Bodine and Boell, 1934 *b*; Robbie, Boell and Bodine, 1938). The growing post-diapause embryo is also sensitive to carbon monoxide poisoning. A gas mixture containing 90% carbon monoxide to 10% oxygen reduces the respiration by one-half while slightly stimulating the respiration of diapause embryos (Bodine and Boell, 1934 *a*). The development of the post-diapause embryos is checked by carbon monoxide but growth is again resumed after exposure to strong light (Allen, 1940).

These results show that the cytochrome–cytochrome-oxidase system is required for growth but is not concerned in maintaining the metabolism in the diapause embryo. Yet cytochrome oxidase is present in the diapause embryo. The enzyme increases in concentration with the size of the embryo and is present throughout diapause (fig. 22 A) (Bodine and Boell, 1936; Allen, 1940). Cyanide stability seems therefore to result from the inactivity of the enzyme rather than from its absence. Bodine, Lu and West (1952) have also observed that the

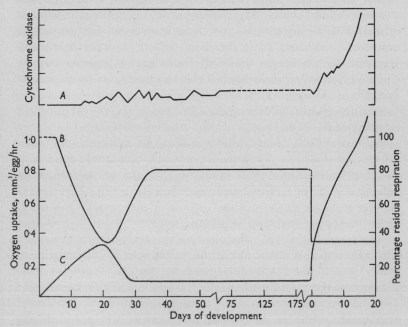

Fig. 22. Cyanide-stable and cyanide-sensitive respiration in *Melanoplus differentialis*. A, the relative concentration of cytochrome oxidase in the embryo throughout development (after Allen). B, and right-hand ordinate, the residual respiration of eggs treated for three hours with 0·001 M KCN. C, and left-hand ordinate, oxygen consumption of control eggs (after Robbie, Boell and Bodine). Diapause period from 21 to 180 days.

respiration of homogenates prepared from diapause embryos is considerably stimulated by the addition of sodium succinate and that this induced respiration is inhibited by cyanide. These experiments also suggest that the succinoxidase system is intact in the diapause embryo but is not fully functional. This view is also held by Wolsky (1949) who has observed that the unfertilized and the diapausing eggs of *Bombyx* are both characterized by a similar cyanide-stable respiration.

The extensive researches of Williams and his co-workers, who have used the pupa of the giant silkmoth *Platysamia cecropia* as material, have greatly extended our knowledge of the enzymatic changes associated with growth and diapause. The metabolism of the diapausing pupa is again of the carbon monoxide and cyanide-stable type. Short exposures to carbon monoxide readily kill the eggs, larvae or adult insects but the pupae are resistant, although they are soon killed once imaginal differentiation has begun (Schneiderman and Williams, 1954 *b*). Cecropia pupae will withstand the implantation of crystals of potassium cyanide. Considerable resistance is also shown to inhibitors such as pilocarpine which block the synthesis of one or more of the components of the cytochrome system. Dormant pupae are resistant to the injection of 70 μg. of diphtheria toxin, whereas a dose of 1 μg. immediately inhibits larval growth or adult differentiation. This toxin is thought of as competing selectively for the iron-containing prosthetic groups by virtue of its resemblance to the protein moiety of the cytochrome molecule (Pappenheimer and Williams, 1952).

The respiration of the diapause pupa is only slightly depressed by high concentrations of carbon monoxide and cyanide—an effect which is entirely accounted for by the action of these poisons on the pupal musculature (see below). The metabolism becomes increasingly sensitive to these inhibitors as diapause is terminated. But the CO-stable mechanism is retained during the early stages of adult differentiation, for growth can then be arrested without injury. Carbon monoxide inhibition is fully photoreversible at this time (Schneiderman and Williams, 1954 *a*, *b*). Evidently a metabolism mediated by cytochrome oxidase is necessary for growth but is not required for the maintenance of the diapausing pupa.

Spectroscopic studies have revealed that in addition to the classical cytochromes *b*, *c* and $a + a_3$, a further component, b_5 (b_x) is of considerable functional importance in *Platysamia* and indeed is probably the terminal oxidase in the pupa (Sanborn and Williams, 1950; Shappirio and Williams, 1953). This haemoprotein, absorbing at 552 mμ, is now considered to be

96

identical with cytochrome *e* previously described by Keilin and Hartree (1949). The properties of b_5 have been investigated by Pappenheimer and Williams (1953). It is autoxidizable and is therefore unaffected by inhibitors of cytochrome oxidase such as cyanide, carbon monoxide or antimycin *A*. *In vitro* it can function as a terminal oxidase and is capable of transferring electrons from pyridine nucleotide-flavoprotein to molecular oxygen.

In the cecropia larva cytochrome b_5 is the principal enzyme in the mid-gut and other tissues, *b* and *c* being present only as minor elements in the heart and muscles. b_5 is also present in all the tissues of the diapause pupa, but none of the other components can be detected except in the intersegmental muscles of the abdomen which possess an intact cytochrome system. In the adult moth large concentrations of *b*, *c* and $a + a_3$ appear in the flight muscles but there are only traces of b_5. The selective action of respiratory poisons on the different tissues of the pupa affords an interesting confirmation of the results of spectroscopic analysis. In pupae treated with cyanide or carbon monoxide heart activity remains unimpaired since the respiration of this organ is mediated by b_5; but the intersegmental muscles, which retain a functional cytochrome oxidase, degenerate. The increased rate of water loss from the pupa also suggests that the spiracular muscles are similarly affected.

These studies show that the low diapause metabolism of the pupa is especially associated with the presence of cytochrome b_5 and with the absence of *c*, save in the musculature. This system appears to be incompatible with growth. When diapause is terminated, the resumption of morphogenesis and even, at this stage, the maintenance of life, seems to be dependent upon the rapid synthesis and utilization of cytochrome *c* and cytochrome oxidase. It will be noted that this conception differs from the explanation advanced for *Melanoplus* and *Bombyx* in which the development of a cytochrome-mediated respiration has been attributed to the 'recoupling' of a cytochrome system already present in the diapause egg, not to its synthesis.

It is also noteworthy that the qualitative changes in the enzyme systems of *Platysamia* are quite distinct from the quantitative changes which are a feature of the developing

7   97

non-diapause pupa (Wolsky, 1938). The U-shaped curve of oxygen consumption in the metamorphosing pupa seems to be closely related to the total concentration of cytochromes present, since the same fraction of the respiration remains susceptible to inhibitors irrespective of the changes in respiratory intensity. If these differences are of general occurrence in species with a facultative pupal diapause, for example, in *Deilephila* (p. 91), the apparent resemblance of the falling curves of oxygen uptake in the diapause and non-diapause pupae must be regarded as entirely superficial.

Although the diapause metabolism of *Platysamia* and *Melanoplus* is of the cyanide-stable type, this is by no means universal. Dormant larvae of *Gastrophilus* taken in winter from the gastric mucosa of the horse are readily killed by cyanide and carbon monoxide (Levenbook, 1951 *b*). Hibernating *Leptinotarsa* are also cyanide-sensitive (Precht, 1953). The larch sawfly *Pristophora erichsonii* is comparatively resistant to cyanide at all stages of development; nevertheless, the resistance is not enhanced as the insect enters diapause in the prepupal stage (MacDonald and Brown, 1952). Cytochrome oxidase activity in the larva of *Popillia japonica* is higher during the 50 days diapause period in the 3rd instar than at any other time during growth and metamorphosis (Ludwig, 1953). It seems that in these insects the metabolic adjustments during diapause do not involve any appreciable changes in the activity of cytochrome oxidase.

In general, it is to be expected that the intracellular enzyme systems will be adapted to the particular needs of the organism during the diapause period. Insects which remain mobile, or even display migratory activity (p. 89), will require a more vigorous oxidative metabolism than those which pass the dormant period as an immobile egg or pupa. Even in *Platysamia*, a fully functional musculature is required to control the opening of the spiracles and to flex the abdominal segments; in these tissues, as we have seen, the cytochrome system is retained intact.

Metabolic Adjustment in the Dormant Insect

The enzymatic adaptations described in the preceding pages are in turn evoked by agencies external to the cells. When diapause occurs in the post-embryonic stages of morphogenesis, these adjustments are co-ordinated by humoral means; in the egg they are perhaps induced by comparatively simple changes in the physical properties of the medium surrounding the embryo.

In the egg of *Melanoplus* a functional cytochrome system is re-established and mitosis resumed, when the medium bathing the embryo is diluted with water under well-aerated conditions (Slifer, 1946; Bucklin, 1953). It may not be inappropriate to compare this phenomenon with the induced biosynthesis of enzymes in some micro-organisms. In general, the synthesis of the enzyme is dependent upon the presence of some specific substance in the environment. This is usually a substrate but it may also be oxygen. For example, it is well known that cytochrome oxidase synthesis fails and the enzyme itself eventually disappears when yeasts are cultured anaerobically. Under these conditions a continuous multi-enzyme system of electron transfer is broken, leaving some catalysts isolated and apparently non-functional (Slonimsky, 1953).

In the pupa of *Platysamia* the restitution of a metabolism mediated by cytochrome oxidase is controlled by the organs of internal secretion, notably the brain and prothoracic glands (Williams, 1948). The synthesis of cytochrome c and cytochrome oxidase cannot be initiated until the tissues have been activated by the prothoracic glands. Only about 1 week afterwards does the continued synthesis of these haemoproteins become independent of the hormone. The opposing process, namely, the substitution of the enzyme systems of diapause for those characteristic of the growing larva, is evoked by the withholding of the prothoracic gland hormone. In saturniids with a facultative pupal diapause, such as the bivoltine *Actias luna* and the multivoltine *A. selene*, the diapause metabolism can readily be elicited if the activation of the prothoracic glands is prevented by brain removal shortly after pupation. This effect is secured even if the pupae have been determined initially for uninterrupted growth (Williams, 1952a).

Since there is clear evidence that metabolic adaptation is controlled by humoral or other means, these changes are evidently secondary so far as the causation of diapause is concerned. At the same time, the possession of the appropriate intracellular mechanisms must certainly be regarded as one of the fundamental attributes of the diapausing insect. This point may be illustrated by comparing the survival of an insect which is prevented from growing by operative means with a similar species possessing a diapause. Fully fed larvae of *Lymantria dispar* deprived of their brains on the 7th day after the last moult, fail to pupate and eventually die when their store of fat is exhausted. Nevertheless, the maximum duration of this 'artificial diapause' is only 31 days (Kopeć, 1922). As we have seen in Chapter 4, other insects diapausing as fully grown larvae can survive for many months. Evidently the final instar larva of *Lymantria* does not possess the mechanism required for reducing the metabolism to a level compatible with the economical utilization of the reserves. The unhatched larva—the diapause stage in *Lymantria*—does have this faculty and survives for as long as 14 months (Kozhantshikov, 1950a).

CHAPTER 8

THE HUMORAL CONTROL OF DIAPAUSE

It has been known for many years that insects suffer an arrest of growth when deprived of the source of the moulting hormone. The resemblance of this condition to the natural state of diapause was first pointed out by Wigglesworth in 1934. When the *Rhodnius* nymph is decapitated immediately after a blood meal, the bug may remain alive for over a year, but it cannot moult or grow in the absence of the brain. In the light of this experiment Wigglesworth suggested that the temporary failure of a growth-promoting hormone secreted by the brain or other endocrine centre might be a frequent cause of arrested growth in other insects. This view has since been confirmed in a number of species with a larval or pupal diapause; and there is little doubt that this principle will be found to apply to imaginal diapause. Humoral regulation has also been demonstrated in one species with an embryonic arrest, namely, the silkworm *Bombyx mori*. As different endocrine systems are concerned in embryonic, larval-pupal and imaginal diapause, it will be convenient to consider their mode of operation separately.

THE HUMORAL REGULATION OF DIAPAUSE IN *BOMBYX*

It will be recalled that the type of egg laid by the bivoltine strains is decided in the main by the conditions of temperature and photoperiod which prevail during the late embryonic development of the maternal generation (p. 32). Yet despite the early initiation of the processes controlling the voltinism, the fate of the eggs themselves is still undetermined in the late larva or pupa. This was first demonstrated by ovarian transplantation (Umeya, 1926). For example, when ovaries obtained from larvae hatched at 15° C. (these may for simplicity be referred to as 'non-diapause' ovaries) were transplanted into 5th-instar larvae that had been hatched at 29° C. ('diapause' larvae), the resulting moths yielded only diapause egg batches. And a similar reversal of function was secured with reciprocal transplantations. These results, which strongly suggested that the character of the eggs was determined by a hormone circulating in the haemolymph of the pupa and female moth, provided the physiological explanation of the earlier observations of Toyama (1912) and Tanaka (1924) on the maternal inheritance of voltinism (p. 42).

The humoral basis of diapause has since been studied by Fukuda and Hasegawa in a long series of investigations. It was first noticed that the presumptive voltinism could also be changed by decapitation shortly after the pupal moult; headless 'non-diapause' pupae often yielded moths laying diapause egg batches, whereas 'diapause' pupae often developed into moths laying mixed egg batches. Subsequent dissection of the headless moths determined as non-diapause egg-producers revealed that eggs of this type were only laid if the brain was left intact. In the absence of the brain, but with the ganglia of the ventral cord remaining, the moths laid dark diapause eggs (Fukuda, 1951 *a, b*).

Besides establishing the importance of the brain, the results of this experiment indicated that some endocrine centre lying behind the brain was also concerned in the reversal of voltinism —a centre eventually identified as the suboesophageal ganglion. The activity of this organ which, like the brain itself, contains neurosecretory cells, was confirmed by implanting the ganglia into intact 5th-stage 'non-diapause' larvae. A few of the moths so obtained still laid pale eggs, but the majority laid either wholly diapause or mixed egg batches (Fukuda, 1951 *b, c*; Hasegawa, 1952). If the suboesophageal ganglion is indeed contributing a 'hibernation hormone' which diverts the developing eggs towards the diapause condition, it would seem that this factor is withheld in insects previously determined as 'non-diapause'. Confirmation of this view was secured by extirpating the suboesophageal ganglion in pupae determined for the production of diapause eggs. The resulting moths invariably laid non-diapause eggs (Fukuda, 1952).

The hypothesis advanced by Fukuda (1951 *b*) to account for

these and other findings may be summarized as follows. The character of the eggs is determined by the release of the suboesophageal hormone. When the ovaries are exposed to the influence of this product, egg development is of the diapause type; in its absence only non-diapause eggs are formed. The liberation of the hormone depends in turn upon the brain which either restrains the liberation of the hormone in insects destined to lay non-diapause eggs or causes its release in 'diapause' insects. This influence is exerted through the circumoesophageal commissures.

The role of the brain in this endocrine unit has been demonstrated in several ways. (i) Suboesophageal ganglia from either 'non-diapause' or 'diapause' donors prove to be active when tested in 'non-diapause' hosts, although the former may be somewhat weaker. In the case of the 'non-diapause' implant, the inhibiting influence of the brain has evidently been lost. (ii) When 'non-diapause' pupae are deprived of the brain the resulting moths lay diapause or mixed egg batches. However, it is unlikely that the brain controls the suboesophageal ganglion by means of a diffusible hormone for (iii) brain removal followed by immediate reimplantation in 'non-diapause' pupae also converts the insects to the diapause condition. Further, (iv) 'non-diapause' larvae receiving brain implants from 'diapause' donors never give rise to moths laying diapause eggs. The brain therefore ceases to be active when its connectives are severed.

The mode of interaction of brain and suboesophageal ganglion was also shown very beautifully by implanting them either separately or with the connectives intact. When these organs, after removal from a 'non-diapause' donor, are transplanted as a single unit into a 'non-diapause' recipient, the brain continues to exercise its restraining influence in the new environment; the host therefore lays only non-diapause eggs. But when the connectives are cut and the organs implanted separately, the egg batches are predominantly diapause or mixed. Unilateral transection produces a much weaker effect (Fukuda, 1953*c*).

It is less certain whether the brain merely ceases to inhibit the suboesophageal ganglion in the insect destined for diapause or whether it stimulates the synthesis or release of the product. The latter alternative is suggested by the fact that the suboesophageal ganglion appears to lose in potency when isolated from the brain. For example, if the brain is removed from pupae determined for diapause, nearly one-third of the resulting moths lay non-diapause egg batches.

The humoral regulation of voltinism has also been investigated in a univoltine race with obligatory diapause and in a multivoltine race almost free of diapause (Fukuda, 1953a, b). The mode of action of the endocrine system is very like that in the bivoltine silkworm, except that the brain invariably activates the suboesophageal ganglion in the univoltine pupa and almost invariably restrains the liberation of the active principle in the multivoltine insect. Fukuda regards these functions as taking place without reference to the environment (although in Kambodge, the multivoltine strain used, a few moths lay diapause eggs under extreme conditions, notably light incubation at 26° C.). However, on the basis of the arguments set out in a previous chapter (p. 44), it may be preferable to regard the environment as instrumental in determining the brain function even in these races.

The potentialities of the suboesophageal ganglia are the same in all races of *Bombyx*. If the connexions with the brain are severed, the ganglion of a multivoltine insect has the same capacity to release the diapause factor as those of a univoltine or bivoltine insect. The product of the suboesophageal ganglion is neither sex- nor species-specific. Ganglia from male *Bombyx* and from female *Lymantria dispar*, *Antheraea yamamai* and *Dictyoploca japonica* all induce the production of many diapause or mixed egg batches when implanted in 'non-diapause' larvae of *Bombyx*. These Lepidoptera also possess an egg diapause. It is remarkable that the suboesophageal ganglion from *Antheraea pernyi*, a species with a pupal diapause, also possesses this activity. Ganglia from *Philosamia cynthia* with a pupal diapause, and *Dendrolimus pini* with a larval diapause, were found to be inactive (Fukuda, 1951c; Hasegawa, 1952).

The Humoral Control of Diapause

Although it is known that the diapause mechanism in the egg of *Bombyx* is operated by the maternal endocrine system, the more immediate causes of the arrest of growth remain uncertain. It is usually assumed by Japanese workers that a 'hibernation substance' or 'voltinism determiner', perhaps now to be identified with the product of the suboesophageal ganglion, is absorbed by the egg while the latter is still within the ovary. This substance is regarded as a growth inhibitor which is gradually consumed as the egg is chilled. Nevertheless, this is only one of several possible interpretations. For example, the failure of embryonic growth may be due, not to the persistence of the hormone, but to the fact that the physical conditions within the egg are unsuitable for morphogenesis. The nature of the unfavourable factor may vary in different species, but the water content and oxygen tension are two possibilities. If these conditions are under the active control of the egg itself (or, more precisely, of the extra-embryonic tissues), the role of the hormone may be to evoke these powers of regulation.

Evidence favouring the view that the immediate causes of embryonic diapause are not necessarily humoral in nature has recently been secured in the egg of *Melanoplus differentialis*. Bucklin (1953) has shown that the embryos of this grasshopper can be cultured as 'explants' in a hanging drop of Ringer's solution. When diapausing, half-grown embryos, together with their attached yolk mass, are exposed to these conditions (after removal from the chorion and cuticles), the growth arrest is terminated within a few hours and development then proceeds *in vitro* almost to the point of hatching. Young pre-diapause embryos develop through the normal morphogenetic diapause stage without any interruption. Whole or half-embryos which have been freed from yolk will also resume development. And even small yolk-free fragments, such as isolated limb rudiments, show the recrudescence of mitotic activity which is the first indication of the resumption of growth. Evidently the causes for arrest do not reside either within the embryo itself or within the yolk. Nor is there any indication of the presence of an inhibitor in the fluid bathing the embryo. On the contrary, each individual cell in the diapausing embryo seems to be capable of responding at any time if the conditions favourable for growth, notably the free access to water, are restored.

The mode of action of low temperature on the egg is in doubt. Slifer (1948) has suggested tentatively that in the *Melanoplus* egg the waxy layer which protects the hydropyle and prevents the imbibition of water during the dormant period (see p. 71) may be gradually destroyed either by micro-organisms in the soil or by a slow process of weathering. However, the regularities of diapause development suggest that some less casual process must be involved. Perhaps this is a function which is acquired by the hydropyle cells as a result of chilling.

THE HUMORAL CONTROL OF DIAPAUSE IN LARVAE AND PUPAE

The endocrinology of diapause has been extensively studied by Williams, using the pupae of the giant silkmoth *Platysamia cecropia* as material. Under normal circumstances the arrest of growth is brought to an end by chilling, the completion of diapause development requiring about 6 weeks at 5° C. or over 5 months at 25° C. When an intact unchilled pupa is joined to a pupa which has been chilled for an adequate period, both members of the pair resume development promptly at room temperature. This result at once suggests that the arrest is caused by the lack of a growth factor in the blood; if an inhibitory principle were present one would expect the development of the chilled pupa to be delayed (Williams, 1946).

The failure of growth in the diapausing pupa is due primarily to the absence of the hormone secreted by the brain. In Lepidoptera which do not possess a pupal diapause this active principle is liberated soon after pupation and at all temperatures within the morphogenetic range. But in *Platysamia* the brain is inactive until the pupa has first been chilled. Immediate development is only secured if this humoral deficiency is made good by implanting a brain from a chilled pupa. Conversely, pupae which have been deprived of the brain remain in permanent diapause until they die from water loss one or two years after the operation.

The Humoral Control of Diapause

The prothoracic glands are also required for metamorphosis. When brainless diapausing pupae are divided transversely behind the thorax, the anterior portion will resume development if a chilled brain is implanted, while the abdominal fragment, which lacks prothoracic glands, remains unaffected. However, the isolated abdomen will undergo imaginal differentiation if it is connected by means of a plastic tube to a developing anterior half, or if a chilled brain and prothoracic glands are implanted together (Williams, 1947).

In this system the brain is the prime mover and activates the prothoracic glands by means of a diffusible hormone liberated into the blood. Once this activation is complete imaginal differentiation will go forward in the absence of the brain. The product of the prothoracic glands in turn supplies the necessary stimulus to the tissues so that the normal non-diapause metabolism is re-established and all the complex events associated with the inception of the moulting cycle are set in train.

For more detailed information of the mode of action of this endocrine system the reader is referred to a monograph in this series by V. B. Wigglesworth (1954). As the brain and prothoracic glands play so general a role in the regulation of growth in the Insecta, it is to be expected that this will prove to be the controlling system in many other species with a larval or pupal diapause. Some further examples have indeed been described. In *Actias selene*, a bivoltine saturniid, precisely the same sequence of events is observed as in *Platysamia* provided the insect has been determined for diapause: the brain becomes dormant at the beginning of the pupal instar and then requires the stimulus of low temperature. But if the pupa is destined to develop without diapause, brain activity persists and in due course the prothoracic glands are reactivated (Williams, 1952 a).

Church (1953) has shown by ligaturing experiments that endocrine centres in the head and thorax are concerned in the pupation of the sawfly *Cephus cinctus* after the larval diapause has been ended by chilling. The brain and prothoracic glands participate in the control of diapause in the larva of *Sialis lutaria* (Rahm, 1952). The temporary failure of the brain hormone also appears to be responsible for dormancy in the cricket *Gryllus campestris* (Sellier, 1949). The penultimate (9th) nymphal instar in *Gryllus* often lasts for 25–30 days at 30° C., whereas the 8th instar is completed in 6–8 days and the 10th in 10–15. It is significant that the diapause instar is greatly curtailed if the insect is supplied with brain implants from either 7th, 8th or 10th instar nymphs.

THE ENDOCRINE CENTRES RESPONSIVE TO CHILLING

There is little doubt that in *Platysamia* the site of action of low temperature is the brain itself. It has not yet proved possible to chill a living brain *in vitro*. Nevertheless, unchilled brains that are transplanted into brainless diapausing pupae become competent to liberate the hormone after the latter have been chilled for an adequate period at 5° C. Competence to secrete the hormone can therefore be acquired in the absence of the normal afferent nerve supply to the brain (Williams, personal communication). Further, low temperature is not known to influence any organ other than the brain. Thus when a brainless pupa is chilled, and is then supplied with an unchilled brain implant, no development will ensue. Unchilled prothoracic glands are no less effective than chilled glands; both respond similarly to the brain hormone (Williams, 1947).

The humoral activity of the brain, as in other insects, is associated with the presence of neurosecretory cells. There are two groups of these specialized neurones in *Platysamia*, a medial group of eight in the pars cerebralis and a group of five in the lateral region of the cerebral lobe. No other regions of the chilled brain display any activity when tested in a brainless diapausing pupa (Williams, 1952*b*). Although histological examination has revealed the usual signs of neurosecretion—the accumulation of secretory droplets within the cells and their discharge along the axons—the identity of this visible product with the active principle in question has not yet been established in an insect with diapause. The cycles of secretion of different cells are normally out of phase in the diapausing *Platysamia*; and there is no indication that the cycles become synchronous when a chilled pupa is exposed to high temperature (Williams, personal communication).

Physiological methods of assay show nevertheless that it is

helpful to distinguish two stages in the liberation of the brain hormone: the first is the development of competence to secrete the hormone (this is in essence the process referred to in this monograph as diapause development); the second is the subsequent release of this hormone into the haemolymph (Williams, 1952 *b*). The first process is favoured by moderately low temperatures, the second by high temperatures. For example, at 5° C. diapause development eventually proceeds to completion but very little hormone is released. On the other hand, the liberation of the active principle is rapidly effected when the adequately chilled pupa is placed at 25° C. and, since this temperature also favours morphogenesis, development is immediately resumed. The fact that the chilled brain becomes inactive after about 17 days at 25° C. also suggests that the hormone is stored and then discharged.

One may infer that if the *Platysamia* pupa were chilled at a rather higher temperature, the synthesis and release of the brain hormone would go forward concurrently. If the temperature were also compatible with morphogenesis, metamorphosis would eventually take place when the concentration of hormone in the blood reached the threshold required to activate the prothoracic glands. But in this case the resumption of growth would be limited by the slow rate of synthesis and not by the rate of release of the stored product.

High temperatures of 35 or 40° C. also favour the release of the brain hormone in *Cephus cinctus* after diapause development has been completed at 10° C. But although pupation is greatly accelerated during the first 2 days of post-diapause development, longer exposures result in the reinstatement of diapause (Salt, 1947; Church, 1953). The mode of action of high temperature is not fully understood. Nevertheless, it is known that the brain, which becomes dormant after the insect has been returned to diapause, regains its competence to secrete hormone if it is chilled for a second time. Somewhat similar effects have been described in *Lucilia* by Mellanby (1938).

In these and probably many other species the brain is responsible both for the initial interruption in the cyclical activity of the endocrine system and also for the resumption of activity after exposure to cold. Nevertheless, the brain is not invariably the master organ. In *Sialis*, for example, this role appears to have been assumed by the prothoracic glands (Rahm, 1952). After the 10th-instar larvae of *Sialis* have entered diapause in October, a period of low temperature is necessary for the completion of diapause development. If October larvae are ligatured behind the head and are then chilled at 4° C. for 40 days, they always pupate promptly when subsequently returned to room temperature. Since other experiments by Rahm had shown that the prothoracic glands require a stimulus from the brain, just as in other insects, this result suggested that these organs had already been activated by the brain before the onset of diapause. This was confirmed by removing the brain from December larvae that had experienced an adequate period of chilling. No delay in pupation was observed. It seems therefore that in this species low temperature promotes either the synthesis or liberation of stored hormone of the prothoracic glands.

The renewal of humoral activity may sometimes be limited by a further factor, namely, water lack. This is probably true of the hibernating larvae of *Chilo simplex* (Koidsumi, 1952) and possibly of many other species (see Chapter 5). In general, however, the effects of partial dehydration on the physiology of the larval and pupal endocrine system remain to be investigated.

THE HUMORAL CONTROL OF IMAGINAL DIAPAUSE

Reproductive dormancy, involving the reversion of the ovaries to the resting condition, is perhaps the most striking feature of imaginal diapause. It is well known that egg production and the enlargement of the male accessory reproductive organs are often regulated by humoral means in insects that lack a diapause. In *Rhodnius*, for example, neither of these functions can proceed in the absence of the corpus allatum (Wigglesworth, 1936). And in *Calliphora* both the corpus allatum and the neurosecretory cells of the brain are implicated in the control of ovarian development (Thomsen, 1952). These considerations suggest that imaginal diapause may be associated with the failure of the insect to secrete the necessary gonadotrophic hormones.

This type of relationship has been demonstrated by Joly (1945) in the beetle *Dytiscus*, a species which shows a well-defined seasonal rhythm of reproduction. In times of reproductive diapause outside the egg-laying season (March in *D. marginalis*, October in *D. semisulcatus*) the oocytes continue to grow up to the point when yolk deposition would normally begin, but are then invaded and broken down by follicle cells. The complete development of the oocytes is dependent upon the activity of the corpus allatum. Eggs can thus be induced to develop to full term at any time by implanting ten pairs of corpora allata; and the ovaries will regress at the height of egg production if these organs are excised. A stimulus from the brain, mediated by the corpus cardiacum, is required for the maintenance of the gonadotrophic activity of the corpus allatum.

In *Leptinotarsa* the oocytes pass through a similar cycle of growth and degeneration while the beetle is in diapause. Towards the close of hibernation yolky eggs are formed in increasing numbers although full maturation is not observed until feeding activity is resumed. Young females which are about to enter diapause in response to a short photoperiod can be induced to lay eggs by implanting six corpora allata from active beetles. But this effect dies away after about 2 weeks if the short-day treatment is continued (de Wilde, 1953, and personal communication). It is possible that a more remote control is also exercised by the brain, for dormant beetles begin to feed and lay eggs if they receive brain implants from active individuals (Grison, 1949).

Hibernation in *Anopheles maculipennis* also appears to be associated with the inactivity of the corpus allatum (Detinova, 1945).

THE ENVIRONMENT AND THE PROGRAMME
OF ENDOCRINE ACTIVITY

The evidence reviewed in the foregoing pages shows that the inception of diapause is commonly associated with the temporary failure of some component of the endocrine system, usually the neurosecretory cells of the brain. In species with an obligatory diapause this failure will recur at the same point in the life history in each generation; in those with facultative diapause the occurrence of the arrest will be decided by such environmental stimuli as photoperiod and temperature acting on some prior stage in the life cycle. But in both cases the arrest of endocrine activity will be preceded by a number of uninterrupted moulting cycles. The manner in which this 'programme' of activity is controlled has received very little attention.

If the neurosecretory cells of the brain retain a sensory function they may well provide an important link between the environment (external or internal) and the endocrine system. It does in fact seem that the brain receives afferent impulses which govern the timing of the moult. In *Bombyx*, for example, experiments involving brain removal and reimplantation have shown that the separate acts of secretion controlling pupation and imaginal differentiation are determined by afferent stimulation some 24 hours before the liberation of the hormone (Bounhiol, 1952 *a*, *b*).

In the case of larval moulting the relevant afferent stimulation might be expected to emanate from proprioceptors registering the distension of the gut or cuticle or the increase in weight. In *Rhodnius* the stimulus to the neurosecretory cells of the brain is known to arise from the stretching of the abdominal wall at feeding. Nymphs which are given a succession of small blood meals therefore fail to moult; and ecdysis is also prevented if the ventral nerve cord is sectioned immediately after a full meal (Wigglesworth, 1934). The last instar larvae of *Bombyx*, *Lymantria* and *Galleria* will not pupate unless they are permitted to feed for a certain minimum period. This corresponds to about 60 % of the time usually spent feeding in *Bombyx*, about 45 % in *Lymantria* and about 36 % in *Galleria*. This also suggests that some stimulus related to the progress of feeding may be concerned (Bounhiol, 1938).

Although such proprioceptive mechanisms could be pictured as the 'fine adjustment' that normally regulates the timing of the moulting cycle, it is scarcely possible that these stimuli can also be responsible for the failure of neurosecretion in the diapausing insect. A careful examination of most insects with facultative diapause would no doubt reveal that the amount of food consumed, the rate of growth, the reserves stored, and the final weight, differed significantly in individuals determined for diapause and in those destined to develop without interruption. However, these differences would probably be slight. Further, there is no evidence that the state of nutrition influences diapause in any way once the prospective fate has been determined by the environment, often many instars prior to the actual arrest of growth.

These considerations suggest rather that the environmental factors acting on the insect during the sensitive period operate a 'switch' mechanism which decides whether the cycles of neurosecretion shall be interrupted, and which also perhaps 'sets' the number of cycles. This is of course a familiar concept in the study of insect metamorphosis. A comparable mechanism for 'counting the instars' must be invoked to explain the constancy of the number of larval instars which precede metamorphosis (Wigglesworth, 1948). It is interesting to note that this function must also be assumed to reside in the central nervous system.

These possibilities are not of course mutually exclusive. Indeed, it may well be that in the insect with a facultative larval or pupal diapause, both mechanisms participate in the regulation of moulting. When growth is uninterrupted, the moulting cycle may perhaps be initiated by proprioceptive stimuli of the type just discussed. On the other hand, the process of determination for diapause may result in the neurosecretory cells becoming refractory to proprioceptive impulses during the critical instar.

Of this intrinsic mechanism almost nothing is known. It is possible that the determining stimulus from the external environment sometimes reaches the brain through afferent pathways. However, results to date with *Antheraea* and *Bombyx* suggest that the central nervous system may itself serve as the primary receptor for photoperiodic stimuli (see pp. 21, 33). The physiological processes involved in 'counting the instars' are entirely obscure. The setting of this mechanism can perhaps be visualized most easily when sensitivity to the environment is restricted to some definite stage of morphogenesis, as in *Diataraxia*. Greater difficulties are encountered when the sensitive period spans several instars as in the case of *Antheraea* and *Grapholitha* (p. 34).

Physiology of Diapause in Arthropods

The view that the central nervous system is the vehicle which carries and eventually transmits the 'directions' of the environment can only be upheld if the interval intervening between the sensitive period and the arrest of growth does not bridge the early stages of embryonic development. This requirement is fulfilled in the majority of examples discussed in Chapter 2. Apparent exceptions are provided by the species *Spalangia*, *Lucilia* and *Phlebotomus*, in which maternal effects seem to be communicated to the larval progeny. If these results are confirmed, an entirely different mechanism of transmission will have to be sought.

Although the question of the determination of brain activity is of primary importance in the present context, some reference must also be made to the secondary physiological changes associated with diapause. For it is clear that many of these changes are established quite early in development and may indeed be set in train during the sensitive period. The following are some of the side effects which have been observed. We have already noted that individuals destined for diapause often build up more abundant reserves (p. 88); and the larval feeding period may be rather longer (e.g. in *Grapholitha*—Dickson, 1949). The rate of growth of the gonads is also sometimes affected. Thus the development of both ovaries and testes is far more retarded in the diapausing larvae of *Pyrausta* and *Chilo* than in other individuals that are about to pupate without diapause (Parker and Thompson, 1927; Fukaya, 1951). The alternative patterns of behaviour that are typical of many insects with facultative diapause must also be considered. These may be comparatively simple, involving changes in the sign of photo- or geotaxis, etc. (e.g. in *Leptinotarsa*, see p. 18). In other instances, however, the differences may be elaborate in the extreme (e.g. in the moth *Amblypalpis tamaricella*—Marikovsky, 1952). Whether these alternative patterns are correlated with the final humoral changes which also control growth, or whether they are linked with some prior event, is still unknown.

The Humoral Control of Diapause

Recent experimental evidence, which has been outlined in this chapter, has fully established the significance of humoral mechanisms in the regulation of diapause. Yet, while this is now accepted by most authorities, opinions differ as to the precise role of the endocrine system in the chain of events which leads to the onset or termination of diapause. Before turning to consider these alternative theories, the conclusions reached in the present monograph may be summarized.

Larval and pupal diapause. The arrest of development is caused by the temporary interruption in the cyclical activities of the endocrine system which normally initiates moulting and growth—the brain and prothoracic glands. The neurosecretory cells of the brain are often, though not invariably, responsible for this failure. It is suggested that the environmental factors which prevent or induce diapause often act more or less directly upon the brain, thereby determining its future pattern of activity. When the hormones required for growth are again secreted, development is resumed. The factors responsible for the termination of diapause, of which low temperature is the most important, also seem to act directly upon these endocrine centres, rendering them competent to resume their cyclical activity.

Imaginal diapause. Reproductive dormancy is probably controlled by the corpus allatum and perhaps, more remotely, by the brain. The relationship of the gonadotrophic hormones with the reproductive organs is direct; diapause supervenes if they are withheld.

Embryonic diapause. When growth is arrested in the early stages of embryogenesis, the control of diapause devolves upon the maternal endocrine system (*Bombyx*). Here the failure of growth is not evoked by the *absence* of a growth-promoting factor but by the *presence* of a hormone in the maternal blood stream at a time when the future condition of the egg is being determined. The relationship between the product of the suboesophageal ganglion and the assumption of the diapause state is pictured as being indirect. The immediate cause of the failure of embryonic development is attributed to the existence of unfavourable physical conditions within the egg. This conforms with the views of Slifer (1946), Umeya (1950) and Bucklin (1953) on the importance of the state of hydration in controlling the diapause in some insect eggs. If the egg possesses the ability to regulate the internal medium, the function of the maternal hormone may be to elicit these active properties. There is as yet no proof that the resumption of growth is controlled by humoral means. The action of low temperature on the egg may be to modify the activities of the extra-embryonic tissues so that the exchanges with the external environment are promoted, and the conditions compatible with growth restored.

When diapause supervenes in the late embryo the means of control may well be entirely different. At this time the embryo possesses its own endocrine centres. The arrest of growth may then be due to a hormone failure, just as in the larva or pupa.

Metabolic theories. Some authors have concluded that external and internal factors influence the onset of diapause through the medium of the metabolism. This view is adopted by Simmonds (1948), who regards diapause as a pathological condition which is brought on when the level of metabolism and general vitality is depressed.

The concept of metabolic control has been further developed by Andrewartha (1952) in his 'food mobilization' hypothesis. This author acknowledges the probability that in larval or pupal diapause the immediate cause of the arrest is the temporary absence of the hormones required for growth. But he suggests that the environmental stimuli which determine the onset of diapause, and control its termination, influence the neuro-secretory cells of the brain indirectly through the medium of the tissues associated with the storage of the food reserves. According to the hypothesis, the necessary stimulus to the brain or other growth centres is supplied by the easily assimilated breakdown products of the fat body or egg yolk. In the insect destined to develop without interruption the stimulatory mechanism is evoked when a certain prerequisite amount of food has been ingested and metabolized. But in the individual determined for diapause the different pattern of metabolism results in the accumulation of an 'intractable' food reserve which can only be broken down after an adequate exposure to some stimulus such as low temperature.

The physiological evidence at present available does not favour this theory. There can be little doubt that in *Platysamia* low temperature affects the brain directly. As we have seen (p. 108), an implanted brain can be rendered competent to liberate the hormone by chilling; yet chilled brainless pupae are not competent to activate an implanted unchilled brain. These facts must prove conclusive when taken in conjunction. Experiments by Bucklin (1953) on *Melanoplus differentialis* have also shown that the presence of unmetabolized yolk has no restraining influence on embryonic growth (see p. 105).

The 'intractability' of the food reserves during diapause is to some extent illusory. Although the rate of consumption of the reserves is naturally much lower than in the developing insect, it is nevertheless quite appreciable at high temperatures. The following example may be taken in illustration. In *Malacosoma disstria* (Lasiocampidae) the principal reserves of the fully developed but unhatched larva consist of the plug of yolk filling the stomodaeum and mid-gut. If the larva is held at 25° C. the intestinal wall soon shown signs of secretory activity, and yolk absorption is complete after 3 months (Hodson and Weinman, 1945). Yet in spite of the total mobilization of the yolk, the larva cannot develop further and eventually succumbs to starvation. It is more probable that the rate of mobilization is dependent upon the level of tissue metabolism which is itself determined by humoral or other means.

A metabolic theory of a different type has been proposed by Agrell (1951 *b*). The arrest of growth in the pupae of *Phalera bucephala* is attributed by this author to a defect in the mechanism of decarboxylation induced by a deficiency in thiamine and other vitamins required for the prosthetic groups of decarboxylases. The hormone terminating diapause is regarded as promoting the synthesis of these vitamins. However, positive evidence for this view is still lacking. The injection of these vitamins into the pupae of *Phalera* fails to bring diapause to an end.

Theories postulating growth inhibitors. Diapause has often been attributed to the presence of inhibitory substances. This concept has been developed particularly by Roubaud (1922) who regarded diapause as a state of intoxication brought on by the accumulation of waste products, particularly urates. Despite some later elaborations (Roubaud, 1935), the essentials of this hypothesis were disproved in 1932 when Cousin showed that an insect with facultative diapause (*Lucilia sericata*) could be reared indefinitely without arrest.

Bodine (1932) has postulated that the newly laid egg of *Melanoplus differentialis* contains a fixed quantity of a hypothetical 'diapause factor' which arrests the development of the embryo only when the latter has grown to the diapause stage. This substance is thought of as being inhibited or gradually destroyed by cold. It will be noted, however, that the subsequent observations of Slifer (1946) and Bucklin (1953) on the same egg do not confirm this idea (p. 71). Many Japanese authors are of the opinion that the growth arrest in *Bombyx* is due to an inhibitory 'hibernation substance' or 'voltinism determiner' (Umeya, 1926; Kogure, 1933). Although the product of the suboesophageal ganglion is now known to be capable of changing the voltinism, it is perhaps premature to regard this hormone as an inhibitor which persists within the egg after the inception of diapause (p. 105). In extending the hypothesis of a 'diapause hormone' Hinton (1953b) has recently suggested that the active principle of the suboesophageal ganglion also induces diapause in the pupa, and that this hormone is later antagonized by the prothoracic glands. While it is important that the humoral function of the ganglion should be investigated in this material, the experimental evidence does not at present support the view that growth inhibitors are primarily responsible for pupal arrests (p. 106).

Inherent annual rhythms. In many older studies it was customary to regard diapause as the manifestation, either wholly or in part, of some deep-seated internal rhythm which had been moulded by natural selection until it matched the rhythm of the environment (Pictet, 1913; Babcock, 1927b; Uvarov, 1931; Theodor, 1934). Although this opinion must often have arisen because some significant component of the environment had been overlooked, this possibility cannot entirely be ignored.

Joly (1945) considers that *Dytiscus marginalis* exhibits a fixed seasonal rhythm of this kind, since in his experiments the beetles continued to lay their eggs in March without apparent regard to the external environment. The treatments included extending the day length during winter by 2 hours, exposure to high (30° C.) or low (2–5° C.) temperatures, and regular daily feeding or partial starvation. However, as the possibility that *Dytiscus* responds to the rate of change of day length does not appear to have been excluded, the existence of an innate annual rhythm cannot yet be regarded as established.

CHAPTER 9

DIAPAUSE AND PHENOLOGY

DORMANT arthropods are often better equipped to conserve water than the actively developing stages. This is true, for example, of the diapause eggs of the grasshoppers *Austroicetes cruciata* and *Melanoplus differentialis* (Birch and Andrewartha, 1942; Slifer, 1946). In the winter egg of the mite *Petrobia latens* (Tetranychidae) additional resistance to desiccation is conferred by the thick layer of wax which is lacking in the summer egg (fig. 23) (Lees, 1954). In dormant larvae and pupae water is conserved by the intermittent opening of the spiracles (Punt, 1950; Schneiderman and Williams, 1953).

During diapause many insects also display an enhanced ability to withstand cold. For example, the beetle *Anatolica eremita* lives for only 10 minutes at −15° C. if tested during the autumn feeding period, but survives for 12 hours or more in October after feeding has ceased (Edelman, 1951). But it is doubtful whether this cold hardiness is associated with any fundamental property of the diapause condition. The high undercooling point of the active insect may be connected merely with the presence in the gut of food particles which act as foci for ice formation (Salt, 1953). It is also worthy of note that extreme cold hardiness (the ability to survive the partial freezing of the body fluids) is exhibited both by certain diapausing insects (*Loxostege, Croesus*—Kozhantshikov, 1938*a*) and by other species, such as arctic chironomid larvae, that are merely quiescent (Scholander, Flagg, Hock and Irving, 1953). Evidently, then, the adaptive significance of diapause must lie elsewhere.

It is clear that diapause should be regarded primarily as a timing mechanism. As Andrewartha (1952) has recently emphasized, the usual function of this device is to ensure that the active stages are present when food supplies are plentiful, and when conditions of temperature or moisture are suitable for their development. However, in some species with a short imaginal life the more obvious function is to synchronize adult emergence. It follows that many of the periodic events in insect life are governed directly or indirectly by the diapause relationships. The purpose of the present chapter is to discuss some of the principles which are involved in this type of phenological adjustment.

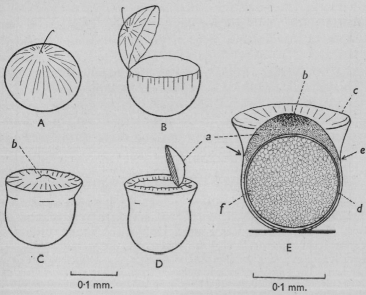

Fig. 23. Form and structure of the eggs of the mite *Petrobia latens*. A, B, summer (non-diapause) egg showing the method of eclosion. C, D, winter (diapause) egg. E, the winter egg viewed in optical section after injection with cobalt naphthenate; the yolky ovum (*f*) is surrounded by two waxy envelopes: the inner layer (*a*) is porous, the outer (*c*) non-porous. Air can only enter the egg through the boss (*b*) in the centre of the cap.

THE REGULATION OF THE LIFE CYCLE

In species with a facultative diapause the season of active growth is limited by the environmental factors which terminate diapause and by those which again evoke diapause. Although the mode of action of these 'calendar' stimuli has already been discussed in Chapters 2 and 4, their operation in nature requires some further comment.

Environmental control may first be illustrated by reference to the red spider mite *Metatetranychus ulmi*. The course of the life cycle in English orchards which are supporting only a small mite population is summarized in fig. 24. The time of hatching of the winter eggs is determined by the temperature conditions prevailing during the previous 5 months. As the eggs require nearly 150 days for the completion of diapause development

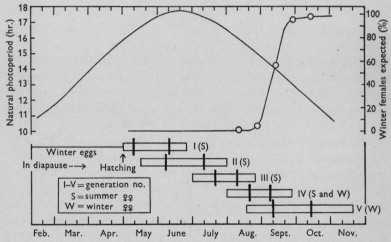

Fig. 24. The life cycle of the mite *Metatetranychus ulmi* in relation to day length (after Lees). The timing of the generations is based on the studies of Blair and Groves (1952); the vertical bars mark the approximate time of appearance of the first and last deutonymphs in each generation.

over the optimum temperature range (1–9° C.), one may infer that this process is proceeding almost continuously from October to March (Lees, 1953 *a*).

The induction of diapause in *Metatetranychus* is controlled by several agencies, including the length of day, temperature and the nature of the food. The question of day length will be considered first. As all light intensities greater than 1–2 f.c. are effective photoperiodically, the operative day length will include periods of dawn and dusk twilight which amount to about 1 hour under English conditions. The seasonal trends shown in fig. 24 have therefore been based on this figure. A second curve giving the proportions of summer and winter females expected with corresponding photoperiods (at a constant temperature of 15° C.) can then be constructed.

Several points emerge from an inspection of fig. 24. The rate of diapause development in the egg is of course adjusted to the climatic conditions, so that hatching is prevented until the foliage has begun to grow. But it will be noted that the long diapause period also serves a further function, namely, that of delaying development of the first deutonymphs (the sensitive stage in *Metatetranychus*) until the day length exceeds the critical duration of about 15 hours. All the first-generation mites therefore develop into females laying summer eggs. The second and third generations should likewise consist of summer females only, since the length of day exceeds 16 hours at all times during their development. On the other hand, winter females would be expected to appear in the fourth generation, and the fifth should consist almost exclusively of mites of this type.

The fact that this pattern of development agrees closely with the observed course of the life cycle suggests that the day-length response is of considerable significance in nature. At the same time there is no doubt that the other agencies mentioned also play a part. Higher summer temperatures would be expected to reinforce the action of the long day length; and lower autumn temperatures will augment the effect of the short day length. When the foliage undergoes senescence in the autumn, the resulting impoverishment of the food supplies is itself a potent diapause-inducing factor (p. 37). At this season all three factors will therefore tend to act in unison. Nevertheless, this seasonal pattern may be considerably disturbed if the mite populations reach outbreak proportions early in the summer. The consequent depletion of the food supplies can overcome even the summated effects of a long photoperiod and high temperature. Indeed, field studies have shown that under these conditions winter females may appear in the third or even in the second generations (Kuenen, 1946; Blair and Groves, 1952).

When the season of active growth is limited by the length of day, temperature may also play an indirect role in controlling the incidence of diapause and the generation number. Researches by Komarova (1949) on the multivoltine eucosmid *Polychrosis botrana* illustrate this principle. There are three generations annually in southern Russia. A variable proportion of the second generation, together with all the third-generation insects enter diapause in the pupal stage. Komarova studied the life cycle in two localities which differed in altitude and therefore in mean summer temperature. Since the latitude was identical, the day length became critical at about the same date, namely,

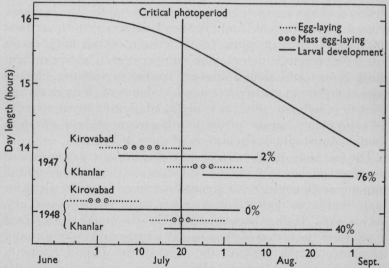

Fig. 25. The influence of day length and temperature on the incidence of diapause in the second annual generation of *Polychrosis botrana* in southern Russia (after Komarova).

20 July. But development was found to be appreciably slower at Khanlar which was the higher and cooler of the two places (fig. 25).

The incidence of diapause in the second generation was markedly influenced by the timing of the light-sensitive egg stage in relation to the critical date. In the year 1947 nearly all the first-generation moths at Kirovabad had deposited their eggs some weeks before 20 July (fig. 25). Accordingly, all except 2% of the second-generation pupae escaped diapause. But at Khanlar cooler conditions delayed oviposition until after this date with the result that 76 % entered diapause. The incidence of diapause also differed from year to year; in the warmer summer of 1948 only 40 % of the Khanlar population entered diapause in this generation.

Similar circumstances probably govern the life cycle in *Cydia pomonella* which responds to a critical day length of 14–15 hours (Dickson, 1949). The codling moth is essentially univoltine in northern France and in England, although a variable proportion of the fully fed larvae (usually under 10 %) fail to enter diapause if the summer is warm. Near Lyons in the south of France the flight period of the first-generation moths in June and July hardly differs from that in the more northerly areas, but their progeny develop about 2 weeks earlier. The pattern of diapause is modified accordingly. About 70 % of these larvae pupate and yield a second generation (Bonnemaison, 1945). In Turkey there are even three generations a year (Seçkin, 1952).

'Long-day' species in which diapause is elicited by short photoperiods, and by low or medium temperatures, are probably particularly numerous (see Chapter 2). With such a response, several generations may be interpolated during the summer and early autumn if the intrinsic rate of development is high. However, as the same photoperiods and temperatures are characteristic of both autumn and spring, the mechanism cannot of course operate successfully unless the insect is unresponsive to the diapause-inducing factors during the early part of the year. The usual safeguard, as we have already noted in *Metatetranychus*, is provided by the processes controlling the release from diapause which delay the onset of active development until the environment is capable of averting diapause. There are, nevertheless, many further variants, of which the following are examples.

Dendrolimus pini. Growth of the larvae remains under the direct control of photoperiod (p. 16). This long-day species therefore enters diapause in autumn and only resumes development in early summer after the day length has extended beyond the critical duration.

Euproctis chrysorrhoea. Diapause is again expressed in terms of the *rate* of larval development, but rapid growth only takes place with photoperiods corresponding to extreme long-day conditions (*c.* 20 hours in the case of a Leningrad population). As the day length has already fallen below the optimum in July when the eggs are hatching, diapause invariably supervenes in the 2nd or 3rd instar. Growth is also delayed in spring. Indeed, according to Gayspitz (1953) the probable function of this mechanism, which results in a univoltine life cycle, is to retard development until the host plants are in full leaf. This will be of particular value in the south where the early spring rise in temperature would otherwise induce premature development.

Bombyx mori. The eggs of this species become sensitive to light and temperature immediately development is resumed in spring. However, the early occurrence of the sensitive period is compensated by the reversal in the direction of the response. Eggs exposed to the short days and low temperatures of spring therefore yield moths laying non-diapause eggs in summer, while the second-generation moths lay eggs of the required diapause type in autumn (Kogure, 1933).

Anax imperator. The same considerations are relevant in the case of this semivoltine dragonfly. The first winter of the life cycle is usually passed as a quiescent half-grown nymph, the second as a final instar nymph in diapause. Although this 2-year cycle is followed by the majority of individuals in nature, 5–10 % of the total population grow more rapidly and, after spending the first winter in late larval instar, enter the final instar (about the 14th) in spring during the months of May and June. These more precocious individuals do not enter diapause but undergo metamorphosis without delay, thereby completing the life cycle in one year (Corbet, 1954). *Anax* seems to become photosensitive shortly after the penultimate ecdysis. As there are some nymphs entering the last instar in both the spring and autumn, the synchronization of adult emergence—the probable function of diapause in this species—could not be achieved if the insect responded simply to the duration of the photoperiod. The available evidence (p. 19) suggests that the progression of the photoperiod is the significant factor: the arrest of growth is averted in spring by the increasing photoperiod but is induced after the summer solstice as the length of day begins to diminish.

In species with an obligatory diapause the timing of the season of active growth is regulated only by the agencies which secure the release from dormancy. As we have seen elsewhere (Chapter 4), temperature is usually the master factor. The most detailed studies on the mode of adjustment of diapause development to the environment are those of Andrewartha (1943, 1952) on the egg of *Austroicetes cruciata*. In South Australia this grasshopper occurs in a restricted climatic belt with a mild winter and a hot dry summer. The development of the eggs, which are laid in November at the beginning of the southern summer, is only completed after nearly 9 months. The spring emergence of the hoppers therefore coincides with the annual flush of the vegetation. During the summer months temperatures are too high to permit any diapause development, and even the slow embryonic growth which occurs during the diapause of this species may be inhibited. However, the diurnal temperature range of autumn is more favourable and the embryo finally reaches the end of anatrepsis by the beginning of winter. As the egg is most sensitive to low temperature at this point in morphogenesis, diapause development now proceeds rapidly and is completed in 2 or 3 months.

This type of environmental control is also common in univoltine species from temperate climates. Hibernation is then preceded by a more or less lengthy period of aestivation. Diapause may actually be no more intense than in multivoltine species which do not aestivate; the longer dormant period may merely be due to the fact that diapause development is completely in abeyance during the summer months. The latter process is usually completed most rapidly during the autumn and winter, but if the winters are severe, the most favourable seasons are autumn and spring (Zolotarev, 1947).

The temperatures at which diapause disappears are relatively low in these insects, so that the requirements are only matched by the environmental conditions during autumn, winter or spring. However, when a somewhat higher effective thermal range is coupled with a diapause of no great intensity, the insect may be released from dormancy 'prematurely' in autumn. This aberrant type of life cycle is found in the winter moth. The eggs of *Operophtera brumata* hatch in March and April and the larvae are fully fed by mid-June, in which month they enter the soil to pupate. The pupal diapause is completed in

120 days at 10° C. or in 145 days at 16° C. Very few moths
emerge at 17–20° C. and none do so at 27° C., although the
pupae remain alive for several months (Kozhantshikov, 1950*b*).
These thermal requirements account for the progressively later
emergence as the distribution is traced southwards. In northern
Russia the moths fly in late October, while in the Crimea the
flight period is delayed until December, and in Transcaucasia or
Sicily until January or February. It is well known also that the
moths emerge earlier in a cool than in a mild autumn.

PHENOLOGICAL ADJUSTMENT IN
GEOGRAPHICAL RACES

Day length, temperature, and perhaps other indicators of season
also, change progressively with geographical location and particularly with latitude. When the insect has a wide area of distribution, considerable disturbances in the timing of the life cycle
will ensue if the reaction to these stimuli remains constant (as
seems to be the case in *Operophtera*). Nevertheless, it is clear that
these trends are sometimes compensated by inherited differences
in the response. For example, strains are known which differ
slightly, but significantly, in their requirements for diapause
development. In the eggs of *Austroicetes cruciata* from Western
Australia the optimum temperature for the termination of
diapause is 13·5° C.—about 3° higher than in the race from
South Australia. This is correlated with the warmer winters of
these western regions (Andrewartha, 1944). Inspection of
fig. 11 also suggests that the intensity of diapause—as revealed
by the rate of diapause development at the thermal optimum—
may be rather greater in the West Australian race.

It is probable that slight inherited differences affecting the
response to factors evoking the arrest could also be demonstrated in species with a facultative diapause. Although this
possibility has hardly been explored as yet, it may be significant
that the critical day length in populations of the red mite
Tetranychus telarius from Cambridge, England, is about 2 hours
shorter than in those from Leningrad, 8° farther to the north
(Bondarenko, 1950; Lees, 1953*a*). Other factors being equal,
this should mean that the Leningrad mites will begin to enter

128

Diapause and Phenology

diapause about 2 weeks in advance of the more southerly populations.

A more radical phenological adjustment is seen in species which have evolved races with facultative and obligatory diapause. The physiology of these types of arrest has already been discussed in Chapter 3. It remains, however, to consider their selective advantages in different environments. It is, of course, obvious that a facultative diapause will be favourable if there is a long season for active growth, as this will permit the insect to exploit the potentialities of the environment to the full. On the other hand, although a univoltine life cycle can result from the operation of the environment on a species with facultative diapause (as in *Cydia pomonella*), this type of arrest may be deleterious in those parts of the range where some of the first-generation insects escape diapause but where the season for active development is too short to permit a second generation to reach the non-feeding dormant stage. In these areas an obligatory diapause will be favoured by selection.

This view is supported by the observations of Peterson (1947,

TABLE 7. *The influence of temperature on the incidence of diapause in population samples of* Pieris napi *taken from various localities in Fennoscandinavia (from Peterson)*

Note. Uppsala and Borgeby are in southern Sweden (latitude 60° N.); Piteå is in northern Sweden (65° N.); Murjek is in Finland near the Arctic Circle (66° N.).

Locality	Temperature (° C.)	% pupae entering diapause
Uppsala	15·5–18	100
	18 –21	89
	20 –26·5	21
Borgeby	10·5–12	100
	15·5–18	54
	21 –24	79
	24 –26·5	35
Piteå	18 –21	100
	24 –26·5	80
Murjek	15·5–18	100
	18 –21	100
	21 –24	100
	24 –26·5	50

9   129   LDA

1949) on the white butterfly *Pieris napi*. In Austria this species is sometimes trivoltine; in southern Sweden most insects are bivoltine, with emergence peaks in May and July, although a small proportion complete only one generation. In the north of Sweden and Finland *P. napi* is almost exclusively univoltine. There is still a very small second brood but, since the second flight period is delayed until August, this generation must regularly be exterminated. The differences in voltinism are determined in part by the environment and in part genetically. When random samples from these localities are reared, high temperatures tend to prevent diapause more strongly than low. But the efficacy of this factor in averting diapause is much less pronounced in the population from the north (table 7).

It may be inferred that *P. napi* exists in two races with facultative and obligatory diapause. Only those insects with a genotype conferring facultative diapause will be influenced by temperature (and probably photoperiod). The population in southern Fennoscandinavia is evidently heterozygous for these types of arrest. But the genotype for obligatory diapause increases in frequency towards the north where it is favourable for survival.

The history of *Pyrausta nubilalis* in North America may be cited as an illustration of the behaviour of a species introduced by commerce which has not yet attained equilibrium with its new environment. Since its discovery near New York in 1921 the cornborer has gradually extended its range south into the states of Ohio and Indiana and north into Ontario. While the population was at first virtually univoltine, an increasing tendency to produce a second generation has been observed in recent years. Near Toledo in Ohio only 1 % of the first-generation larvae pupated in 1936. By 1939 the figure had risen to 12 % and in parts of Indiana to 28 %. However, the incidence of bivoltinism (or facultative diapause) is by no means equal over the area of distribution but tends to diminish rapidly to the north and east as the season becomes shorter and cooler (Vance, 1939, 1942; Nieswander, 1947; Wishart, 1947).

The comparison of a single generation strain from the Lake States and the homozygous multivoltine strain from New England (see p. 45) has revealed that there are other associated differences which are of phenological significance. The intensity of diapause is weaker in the multivoltine race. Accordingly, the larvae pupate earlier and the flight period is advanced by about 2 weeks (Babcock, 1927*a*; Arbuthnot, 1944). The rate of larval development is also more rapid. These attributes would favour the interpolation of an extra generation before further development is cut off by the environment.

SYNCHRONIZATION OF THE GROWTH CYCLES OF INSECTS AND PLANTS

We have seen in *Metatetranychus* and *Austroicetes* that the dormant period is broadly adjusted so that the active stages are only present when suitable food supplies are available. The phenological relationship may be more critical when the host plant is only susceptible to attack during one brief stage in its growth. For example, the wheat-blossom midge *Contarinia tritici* can only oviposit successfully as the wheat ear is emerging from the sheath. If the ear is still enclosed by the sheath or if the ear itself has become tough, the tissues of the plant prove too hard for the insertion of the delicate ovipositor. As the female lives for little more than 24 hours, the timing of the release from the larval diapause is crucial. If the two events are out of step the insect will be forced to seek alternative and less satisfactory host plants (Barnes, 1953).

Physical factors, especially temperature, acting more or less equally on both insect and plant, may often be responsible for their synchronous development. The role of low temperature in bringing dormancy to a close is probably extremely general. Nevertheless, one would not expect that the thermal requirements would match precisely; it will suffice if the response is similar over the limited range of external conditions which is typical of the normal environment.

The existence of these differences will be revealed if the insect and host plant are exposed to abnormal weather conditions or, more dramatically, if they are introduced into a new environment. The temperature relations of the univoltine tropical silkworm *Eriogyna pyretorum* with its host *Liquidamber formosanum* illustrate this point. The first larval instar is the most critical stage in the life-cycle of this insect, since the larvae will not thrive unless provided with tender young foliage. In the natural habitat in Formosa the moth enters a pupal diapause in April or May. After a period of aestivation, dormancy is terminated during the months of October–December when the mean monthly temperature falls to *c.* 17° C. The emergence of the moths in January and February then coincides precisely with the budding of the *Liquidamber*. When *Eriogyna* and its food plant were introduced into the colder climate of Japan the moths emerged at approximately the same date, since the temperature range compatible with diapause development extends down to nearly 5° C. But the plant was affected differently and remained dormant until May. In order to provide the larvae with suitable food it was necessary to retain the pupae at temperatures above 24° C. until January (Koidsumi and Shibata, 1953).

CONCLUSION

That diapause can be studied from many aspects hardly requires further emphasis. We have noted that the physiologist and biochemist have found favourable, even spectacular, material for investigating many fundamental problems of growth and metabolism. In this concluding chapter we have also seen that questions relating to the control of diapause by the external environment often come within the province of the ecologist. Contributions at each level, the biochemical, the physiological and the ecological, are clearly necessary for a full understanding of the diapause phenomenon.

REFERENCES

ABELOOS, M. (1935). Diapause larvaire et éclosion chez le Coléoptère *Timarcha tenebricosa* Fab. *C.R. Acad. Sci., Paris,* **200**, 2212.

ABELOOS, M. (1941). Diapause embryonnaire inconstante chez le Coléoptère *Timarcha violacea-nigra* de Geer. *C.R. Acad. Sci., Paris,* **212**, 722.

AGRELL, I. (1951*a*). The diapause problem. *Année biol.* **27**, 287.

AGRELL, I. (1951*b*). Pupal diapause caused by a vitamin deficiency. *Nature, Lond.,* **167**, 283.

ALLEN, T. H. (1940). Enzymes in ontogenesis (Orthoptera). XI. Cytochrome oxidase in relation to respiratory activity and growth of the grasshopper egg. *J. Cell. Comp. Physiol.* **16**, 149.

ANDREWARTHA, H. G. (1943). Diapause in the eggs of *Austroicetes cruciata* Sauss. (Acrididae) with particular reference to the influence of temperature on the elimination of diapause. *Bull. Ent. Res.* **34**, 1.

ANDREWARTHA, H. G. (1944). The influence of temperature on the elimination of diapause from the eggs of the race of *Austroicetes cruciata* Sauss, occurring in West Australia. *Aust. J. Exp. Biol. Med. Sci.* **22**, 17.

ANDREWARTHA, H. G. (1952). Diapause in relation to the ecology of insects. *Biol. Rev.* **27**, 50.

ARBUTHNOT, K. D. (1944). Strains of the European Corn Borer in the United States. *Tech. Bull. U.S. Dep. Agric.* no. 869, 20 pp.

ASHBEL, R. (1930). Sul ricambio gassoso della uova di bachi da seta (*Bombyx mori* L.). *Protoplasma,* **11**, 97.

ASHBEL, R. (1932). Sul ricambio gassoso della uova di bachi da seta (*Bombyx mori* L.). II. *Protoplasma,* **15**, 177.

BABCOCK, K. W. (1927*a*). The European corn borer *Pyrausta nubilalis* Hübn. I. A discussion of its dormant period. *Ecology,* **8**, 45.

BABCOCK, K. W. (1927*b*). The European corn borer, *Pyrausta nubilalis* Hübn. II. A discussion of its seasonal history in relation to various climates. *Ecology,* **8**, 177.

BABCOCK, K. W. and VANCE, A. M. (1929). The corn borer in Central Europe. *Tech. Bull. U.S. Dep. Agric.* no. 135, 54 pp.

BAKER, F. C. (1935). The effect of photoperiodism on resting treehole mosquito larvae. *Canad. Ent.* **67**, 149.

BAKER, W. A. and JONES, L. G. (1934). Studies of *Exeristes roborator* (Fab.), a parasite of the European corn borer, in the Lake Erie area. *Tech. Bull. U.S. Dep. Agric.* no. 460, 26 pp.

Physiology of Diapause in Arthropods

BARBER, G. W. (1925). Remarks on the number of generations of the European corn borer in America. *J. Econ. Ent.* **18**, 496.

BARNES, H. F. (1943). Studies of fluctuations in insect populations. X. Prolonged larval life and delayed subsequent emergence of the adult gall midge. *J. Anim. Ecol.* **12**, 137.

BARNES, H. F. (1952). Studies of fluctuations of insect populations. XII. Further evidence of prolonged larval life in the wheat blossom midges. *Ann. Appl. Biol.* **39**, 370.

BARNES, H. F. (1953). Outlines of insect phenology. *Trans. 9th Int. Congr. Ent. Amsterdam*, **2**, 163.

BEAUMONT, G. (1944). Diapause imaginale obligatoire et réactivation chez le Coléoptère *Agelastica alni* Redt. *C.R. Acad. Sci., Paris*, **218**, 213.

BERTANI, G. (1947). Artificial 'breaking' of the diapause in *Drosophila nitens*. *Nature, Lond.*, **159**, 309.

BIRCH, L. C. (1945). Diapause in *Scelio chortoicetes* Frogg. (Scelionidae) a parasite of the eggs of *Austroicetes cruciata* Sauss. *J. Aust. Inst. Agric. Sci.* **11**, 189.

BIRCH, L. C. and ANDREWARTHA, H. G. (1942). The influence of moisture on the eggs of *Austroicetes cruciata* Sauss. (Orthoptera) with reference to their ability to survive desiccation. *Aust. J. Biol. Med. Sci.* **20**, 1.

BLAIR, C. A. and GROVES, J. R. (1952). Biology of the fruit tree red spider mite, *Metatetranychus ulmi* (Koch) in south-east England. *J. Hort. Sci.* **27**, 14.

BODENHEIMER, F. S. and SHULOV, A. (1951). Egg-development and diapause in the Moroccan locust (*Dociostaurus maroccanus* Thnb.). *Bull. Res. Coun. Israel*, **1**, 59.

BODINE, J. H. (1925). Effect of temperature on the rate of embryonic development of certain Orthoptera. *J. Exp. Zool.* **42**, 91.

BODINE, J. H. (1929). Factors influencing the rate of respiratory metabolism of a developing egg (Orthoptera). *Physiol. Zoöl.* **2**, 459.

BODINE, J. H. (1932). Hibernation and diapause in certain Orthoptera. III. Diapause—a theory of its mechanism. *Physiol. Zoöl.* **5**, 549.

BODINE, J. H. (1934). The effect of cyanide on the oxygen consumption of normal and blocked embryonic cells (Orthoptera). *J. Cell. Comp. Physiol.* **4**, 397.

BODINE, J. H. and BOELL, E. J. (1934*a*). Carbon monoxide and respiration. Action of carbon monoxide on respiration of normal and blocked embryonic cells (Orthoptera). *J. Cell. Comp. Physiol.* **4**, 475.

BODINE, J. H. and BOELL, E. J. (1934*b*). Respiratory mechanisms of normally developing and blocked embryonic cells (Orthoptera). *J. Cell. Comp. Physiol.* **5**, 97.

BODINE, J. H. and BOELL, E. J. (1936). Enzymes in ontogenesis (Orthoptera). II. The indophenol oxidase. *J. Cell. Comp. Physiol.* **8**, 213.

BODINE, J. H. and EVANS, T. C. (1932). Hibernation and diapause. Physiological changes during hibernation and diapause in the mud-dauber wasp, *Sceliphron caementarium* (Hymenoptera). *Biol. Bull., Woods Hole*, **63**, 235.

References

BODINE, J. H., LU, K. H. and WEST, W. C. (1952). Succinic dehydrogenase in mitotically active and blocked embryonic cells. *Physiol. Zoöl.* **25**, 109.

BOELL, E. J. (1935). Respiratory quotients during embryonic development (Orthoptera). *J. Cell. Comp. Physiol.* **6**, 369.

BONDARENKO, N. V. (1950). The influence of shortened day on the annual cycle of development of the common spider mite. (In Russian.) *C.R. Acad. Sci. U.R.S.S.* (N.S.), **70**, no. 6, 1077.

BONNEMAISON, L. (1945). Arrêts de développement et diapauses. *Ann. Épiphyt.* **11**, 19.

BONNEMAISON, L. (1948a). Remarques sur la diapause chez un hémiptère: *Eurydema ornatum* L. *C.R. Acad. Sci., Paris,* **227**, 985.

BONNEMAISON, L. (1948b). Détermination du stade auquel se produit le déclenchement de la diapause chez un hémiptère: *Eurydema ornatum* L. *C.R. Acad. Sci., Paris,* **227**, 1052.

BONNEMAISON, L. (1952). Morphologie et biologie de la Punaise ornée du chou (*Eurydema ventralis* Kol.). *Ann. Inst. nat. Rech. agron., Paris,* **2**, 127.

BORTHWICK, H. A., PARKER, M. W. and HENDRICKS, S. B. (1950). Recent developments in the control of flowering by photoperiod. *Amer. Nat.* **84**, 117.

BOUNHIOL, J-J. (1938). Recherches expérimentales sur le déterminisme de la métamorphose chez les Lepidoptères. *Bull. biol., Suppl.,* **24**, 1.

BOUNHIOL, J-J. (1952a). L'achèvement de la métamorphose et la mue imaginale seraient commandés par le cerveau à la fin de la vie larvaire chez *Bombyx mori* L. *C.R. Acad. Sci., Paris,* **235**, 671.

BOUNHIOL, J-J. (1952b). Nature probablement sécrétoire du facteur cérébral conditionnant la mue imaginale de *Bombyx mori* L. *C.R. Acad. Sci., Paris,* **235**, 747.

BOYCE, A. M. (1931). The diapause phenomenon in insects, with special reference to *Rhagoletis completa* Cress. (Diptera: Trypetidae). *J. Econ. Ent.* **24**, 1018.

BRADLEY, W. G. and ARBUTHNOT, K. D. (1938). The relation of host physiology to the development of the Braconid parasite *Chelonus annulipes* Wesmael. *Ann. Ent. Soc. Amer.* **31**, 359.

BROOKES, H. M. (1952). The morphological development of the embryo of *Gryllulus commodus* Walker (Orthoptera: Gryllidae). *Trans. Roy. Soc. S. Aust.* **75**, 150.

BROWNING, T. O. (1952a). The influence of temperature on the completion of diapause in the eggs of *Gryllulus commodus* Walker. *Aust. J. Sci. Res.* B, **5**, 112.

BROWNING, T. O. (1952b). On the rate of completion of diapause development at constant temperatures in the eggs of *Gryllulus commodus* Walker. *Aust. J. Sci. Res.* B, **5**, 344.

BROWNING, T. O. (1953). The influence of temperature and moisture on the uptake and loss of water in the eggs of *Gryllulus commodus* Walker (Orthoptera, Gryllidae). *J. Exp. Biol.* **30**, 104.

BUCKLIN, D. H. (1953). Termination of diapause in grasshopper embryos cultured *in vitro*. *Anat. Rec.* **117**, 539.

BURDICK, H. C. (1937). The effect of exposure to low temperature on the developmental time of embryos of the grasshopper *Melanoplus differentialis* (Orthoptera). *Physiol. Zoöl.* **10**, 156.

BURKHOLDER, J. R. (1934). A quantitative study of respiratory metabolism in single developing eggs (Orthoptera). *Physiol. Zoöl.* **7**, 247.

BUSNEL, R. A. and DRILHON, A. (1937). Étude biochemique du *Leptinotarsa decemlineata* Say pendant l'hivernation. *C.R. Acad. Sci.*, Paris, **124**, 916.

BUXTON, P. A. (1935). Changes in the composition of adult *Culex pipiens* during hibernation. *Parasitology*, **27**, 263.

CHRISTENSEN, P. J. H. (1937). Zur Histologie und Embryologie der überwinterten Eier von *Orgyia antiqua* L. *Zool. Jb.*, *Anat.*, **62**, 567.

CHURCH, N. S. (1953). Initiation of post-diapause development and reinstatement of diapause in *Cephus cinctus* Nort. Thesis submitted for the degree of Master of Science, Montana State College.

CHURCH, N. S. and SALT, R. W. (1952). Some effects of temperature on development and diapause in eggs of *Melanoplus bivittatus* (Say) (Orthoptera: Acrididae). *Canad, J. Zool.* **30**, 173.

COMMON, I. F. B. (1952). Migration and gregarious aestivation in the Bogong moth, *Agrotis infusa*. *Nature, Lond.*, **170**, 981.

CORBET, P. S. (1954). The seasonal ecology of dragonflies. Thesis submitted for the degree of Doctor of Philosophy, Cambridge University.

COUSIN, G. (1932). Étude expérimentale de la diapause des insectes. *Bull. biol.*, *Suppl.*, **15**, 341 pp.

CRAGG, J. B. and COLE, P. (1952). Diapause in *Lucilia sericata* (Mg.) Diptera. *J. Exp. Biol.* **29**, 600.

DANILYEVSKY, A. S. (1939). Experiments on the ecological basis of geographical distribution and acclimatization in *Philosamia cynthia* Dr. (In Russian, English summary.) *Zool. Zh.* **19**, 26.

DANILYEVSKY, A. S. (1948). Photoperiodic reactions of insects in conditions of artificial illumination. (In Russian.) *C.R. Acad. Sci. U.R.S.S.* (N.S.), **60**, no, 3, 481.

DANILYEVSKY, A. S. (1949). The dependence of the geographical distribution of insects on the ecological peculiarities of their life cycles. (In Russian,) *Ent. Oboz.* **30**, 194.

DANILYEVSKY, A. S. (1951). On the conditions favouring a several year diapause in Lepidoptera. (In Russian.) *Ent. Oboz.* **31**, 386.

DANILYEVSKY, A. S. and GAYSPITZ, K. F. (1948). The influence of the daily periodicity of illumination on the seasonal rhythm of insects. (In Russian.) *C.R. Acad. Sci. U.R.S.S.* (N.S.), **59**, no. 2, 337.

DANILYEVSKY, A. S. and GLINYANAYA, Y. I. (1949). On the relationships of the dark and light periods of day in the development of insects. (In Russian.) *C.R. Acad. Sci. U.R.S.S.* (N.S.), **68**, no. 4, 785.

DANILYEVSKY, A. S. and GLINYANAYA, Y. I. (1950). On the influence of the rhythm of illumination and temperature on the origin of diapause in insects. (In Russian.) *C.R. Acad. Sci. U.R.S.S.* (N.S.), **71**, no. 5, 963.

References

DAVID, W. A. L. and GARDINER, B. O. C. (1952). Laboratory breeding of *Pieris brassicae* L. and *Apanteles glomeratus* L. *Proc. R. Ent. Soc. Lond.* A, **27**, 54.

DAVIDSON, J. (1932). Resistance of the eggs of Collembola to drought conditions. *Nature, Lond.*, **129**, 867.

DAVIES, W. M. (1930). Parasitism in relation to pupation in *Lucilia sericata* Meig. *Nature, Lond.*, **125**, 779.

DAWSON, R. W. (1931). The problem of voltinism and dormancy in the Polyphemus moth (*Telea polyphemus* Cramer). *J. Exp. Zool.* **59**, 87.

DETINOVA, T. S. (1945). On the influence of the glands of internal secretion upon the ripening of the gonads and the imaginal diapause in *Anopheles maculipennis*. (In Russian.) *Zool. Zh.* **24**, 291.

DICKSON, R. C. (1949). Factors governing the induction of diapause in the oriental fruit moth. *Ann. Ent. Soc. Amer.* **42**, 511.

DIERICK, G. F. E. M. (1950). Breaking of diapause in the winter egg of the European red spider. *Nature, Lond.*, **165**, 900.

DITMAN, L. P., WEILAND and GUILL, J. H. (1940). The metabolism of the corn earworm. III. Weight, water and diapause. *J. Econ. Ent.* **33**, 282.

DOHANION, S. M. (1942). Variability of diapause in *Melissopus latiferreanus*. *J. Econ. Ent.* **35**, 406.

DOUGLASS, J. R. (1928). Precipitation as a factor in the emergence of *Epilachna corrupta* from hibernation. *J. Econ. Ent.* **21**, 203.

DOUGLASS, J. R. (1933). Additional information on precipitation as a factor in the emergence of *Epilachna corrupta* Muls. from hibernation. *Ecology*, **14**, 286.

DREYER, W. A. (1932). The effect of hibernation and seasonal variation of temperature on the respiratory exchange of *Formica ulkei* Emery. *Physiol. Zoöl.* **5**, 301.

DUCLAUX, M. E. (1869). De l'influence du froid de l'hiver sur le développement de l'embryon du ver à soie, et sur l'éclosion de la graine. *C.R. Acad. Sci., Paris*, **69**, 1021.

EDELMAN, I. M. (1951). The influence of low temperatures on beetles of the family Tenebrionidae. (In Russian.) *Ent. Oboz.* **31**, 374.

EMME, A. M. (1949a). The role of temperature in shaking off the embryonic diapause in the mulberry silkworm, *Bombyx mori*. (In Russian.) *C.R. Acad. Sci. U.R.S.S.* (N.S.), **67**, no. 3, 589.

EMME, A. M. (1949b). The combined action of high and low temperatures on the eggs of the mulberry silkworm. (In Russian.) *C.R. Acad. Sci. U.R.S.S.* (N.S.), **67**, no. 4, 747.

EPHRUSSI, B. (1939). *Génétique Physiologique*. Paris.

EVANS, A. C. (1933). Comparative observations on the morphology and biology of some hymenopterous parasites of carrion-infesting Diptera. *Bull. Ent. Res.* **24**, 385.

FEDOTOV, D. M. (1944). Some observations on the internal state of the imago of *Eurygaster integriceps*. *C.R. Acad. Sci. U.R.S.S.* **42**, no. 9, 408.

FERRIS, G. F. (1919). A remarkable case of longevity in insects (Hem., Hom.). *Ent. News*, **30**, 27.

Physiology of Diapause in Arthropods

FIFE, L. C. (1949). Studies of the diapause of the pink bollworm in Puerto Rico. *Tech. Bull. U.S. Dep. Agric.* no. 977, 26 pp.

FLANDERS, S. E. (1939). A black scale parasite with promising qualities. *J. Econ. Ent.* **32**, 152.

FLANDERS, S. E. (1944). Diapause in the parasitic Hymenoptera. *J. Econ. Ent.* **37**, 408.

FLEMION, F. and HARTZELL, A. (1936). Effect of low temperature in shortening the hibernation period of insects in the egg stage. *Contr. Boyce Thompson Inst.* **8**, 167.

FUKAYA, M. (1950). On the factor inducing the dormancy of the rice borer, *Chilo simplex* Butler. *Trans. 8th Int. Ent. Congr., Stockholm*, p. 223.

FUKAYA, M. (1951). Physiological study on the larval diapause in the rice stem borer, *Chilo simplex* Butler. *Ber. Ōhara Inst.* **9**, 424.

FUKUDA, S. (1951a). Alteration of voltinism in the silkworm by decapitating the pupa. *Zool. Mag. Japan*, **60**, 119.

FUKUDA, S. (1951b). Factors determining the production of non-diapause eggs in the silkworm. *Proc. Imp. Acad. Japan*, **27**, no. 9, 582.

FUKUDA, S. (1951c). The production of the diapause eggs by transplanting the suboesophageal ganglion in the silkworm. *Proc. Imp. Acad. Japan*, **27**, 672.

FUKUDA, S. (1952). Function of the pupal brain and suboesophageal ganglion in the production of non-diapause and diapause eggs in the silkworm. *Annot. zool. jap.* **25**, 149.

FUKUDA, S. (1953a). Determination of voltinism in the univoltine silkworm. *Proc. Imp. Acad. Japan*, **29**, no. 7, 381.

FUKUDA, S. (1953b). Determination of voltinism in the multi-voltine silkworm. *Proc. Imp. Acad. Japan*, **29**, no. 7, 385.

FUKUDA, S. (1953c). Alteration of voltinism in the silkworm following transection of pupal oesophageal connectives. *Proc. Imp. Acad. Japan*, **29**, no. 7, 389.

GANDER, R. (1951). Experimentelle und oekologische Untersuchungen über das Schlüpfvermögen der Larven von *Aëdes aegypti* L. *Rev. suisse Zool.* **58**, 215.

GAYSPITZ, K. F. (1949). Light as a factor regulating the cycle of development of the pine Lasiocampid *Dendrolimus pini* L. (In Russian.) *C.R. Acad. Sci. U.R.S.S.* **68**, no. 4, 781.

GAYSPITZ, K. F. (1953). Reactions of monovoltine butterflies to prolongation of daylength. (In Russian.) *Ent. Oboz.* **33**, 17.

GAYSPITZ, K. F. and KYAO, I. I. (1953). The influence of the length of illumination on the development of certain braconids (Hymenoptera). (In Russian.) *Ent. Oboz.* **33**, 32.

GEERING, Q. A. (1953). The sorghum midge, *Contarinia sorghicola* (Coq.), in East Africa. *Bull. Ent. Res.* **44**, 363.

GEIGY, R. and GANDER, R. (1949). Aeussere Einwirkungen beim Schlüpfen von *Aëdes aegypti* aus dem Ei. *Rev. suisse Zool.* **56**, 332.

GIARD, A. (1902). Sur l'éthologie des larves de *Sciara medullaris* Gd. *C.R. Acad. Sci., Paris*, **134**, 1179.

References

GJULLIN, C. M., HEGARTY, C. P. and BOLLEN, W. B. (1941). The necessity of a low oxygen concentration for the hatching of *Aëdes* mosquito eggs. *J. Cell. Comp. Physiol.* **17**, 193.

GRAHAM, S. A. and ORR, L. W. (1940). The spruce budworm in Minnesota. *Bull. Univ. Minn. Agric. Exp. Sta.* no. 142, 27 pp.

GRISON, P. (1947). Développement sans diapause des chenilles de *Euproctis phaeorrhoea* L. (Lep. Liparides). *C.R. Acad. Sci., Paris*, **225**, 1089.

GRISON, P. (1949). Effets d'implantation de cerveaux chez le Doriphore (*Leptinotarsa decemlineata* Say) en diapause. *C.R. Acad. Sci., Paris*, **228**, 428.

GUELMINO, D. J. (1951). The physiology of *Anopheles maculipennis* during hibernation. An attempt to interpret the phenomenon of gonotrophic dissociation. *Ann. Trop. Med. Parasit.* **45**, 161.

GUENNELON-AUBANEL, G. (1951). Observations sur le cycle évolutif de *Rhynchites coeruleus* de Geer (Col. Curculion.). *C.R. Acad. Sci., Paris*, **232**, 656.

HASEGAWA, K. (1952). Studies on the voltinism in the silkworm, *Bombyx mori* L., with special reference to the organs concerning determination of voltinism. *J. Fac. Agric. Tottori Univ.* **1**, 83.

HELLER, J. (1926). Chemische Untersuchungen über die Metamorphose der Insekten. III. Mitteilung: Über die 'subitane' und 'latente' Entwicklung. *Biochem. Z.* **169**, 208.

HENNEGUY, L. F. (1904). *Les Insectes. Morphologie, reproduction, embryogénie.* Paris.

HINTON, H. E. (1951). A new chironomid from East Africa, the larva of which can be dehydrated without injury. *Proc. Zool. Soc. Lond.* **121**, 37.

HINTON, H. E. (1953a). Some adaptations of insects to environments that are alternately dry and flooded, with some notes on the habits of the Stratiomyidae. *Trans. Soc. Brit. Ent.* **11**, 209.

HINTON, H. E. (1953b). The initiation, maintenance, and rupture of diapause: a new theory. *Entomologist*, **86**, 279.

HODSON, A. C. (1937). Some aspects of the role of water in insect hibernation. *Ecol. Monogr.* **7**, 271.

HODSON, A. C. and WEINMAN, C. J. (1945). Factors affecting recovery from diapause and hatching of eggs of the forest tent caterpillar, *Malacosoma disstria* Hbn. *Tech. Bull. Minn. Agric. Exp. Sta.* no. 170, 31 pp.

HOLDAWAY, F. G. (1927). The bionomics of *Smynthurus viridis* Linn. or the South Australian Lucerne flea. *Pamphl. Coun. Sci. Industr. Res. Aust.* no. 4, 23 pp.

HOLDAWAY, F. G. and EVANS, A. C. (1930). Parasitism a stimulus to pupation: *Alysia manducator* in relation to its host *Lucilia sericata*. *Nature, Lond.* **125**, 598.

JOLY, P. (1945). La function ovarienne et son contrôle humoral chez les Dytiscides. *Arch. Zool. exp. gén.* **84**, 49.

KEILIN, D. and HARTREE, E. F. (1949). Effect of low temperature on the absorption spectra of haemoproteins; with observations on the absorption spectrum of oxygen. *Nature, Lond.*, **164**, 254.

Physiology of Diapause in Arthropods

KEVAN, D. K. M. (1944). The bionomics of the neotropical cornstalk borer, *Diatraea lineolata* Wlk. (Lep. Pyral.) in Trinidad. *Bull. Ent. Res.* **35**, 23.

KOGURE, M. (1933). The influence of light and temperature on certain characters of the silkworm, *Bombyx mori*. *J. Dep. Agric. Kyushu Univ.* **4**, 1.

KOIDSUMI, K. (1952). Water-content and the hormone-centre for the pupation of hibernating larvae of *Chilo simplex* Butler. *Annot. zool. jap.* **25**, 156.

KOIDSUMI, K. and MAKINO, K. (1953). On the mechanism of water absorption in hibernating larvae of the rice-stem borer *Chilo simplex* Butler in spring. *J. Appl. Zool. Japan*, **18**, 1.

KOIDSUMI, K. and SHIBATA, K. (1953). Effects of low temperature upon the termination of aestivation of pupae of a tropical moth (*Eriogyna pyretorum* Westwood). *J. Appl. Zool. Japan*, **17**, 103.

KOMAROVA, O. S. (1949). The conditions evoking diapause in the vine leafroller (*Polychrosis botrana* Schiff.). (In Russian.) *C.R. Acad. Sci. U.R.S.S.* (N.S.), **68**, no. 4, 789.

KOPEĆ, S. (1922). Studies on the necessity of the brain for the inception of insect metamorphosis. *Biol. Bull.*, *Woods Hole*, **42**, 322.

KOZHANTSHIKOV, I. W. (1938*a*). Physiological conditions of cold hardiness in insects. *Bull. Ent. Res.* **29**, 253.

KOZHANTSHIKOV, I. W. (1938*b*). Geographical distribution and physiological characters of *Pyrausta nubilalis* Hb. (In Russian, English summary.) *Zool. Zh.* **17**, 246.

KOZHANTSHIKOV, I. W. (1948). Hibernation and diapause in lepidopterous insects of the family Orgyidae (Lepidoptera, Insecta). (In Russian.) *Bull. Acad. Sci. U.R.S.S.*, biol. ser., no. 6, 653.

KOZHANTSHIKOV, I. W. (1950*a*). Features of the hibernation and diapause of the gipsy moth (*Ocneria dispar* L.). (In Russian.) *C.R. Acad. Sci. U.R.S.S.* (N.S.), **73**, no. 3, 605.

KOZHANTSHIKOV, I. W. (1950*b*). The developmental cycle and geographical distribution of the winter moth *Operophtera brumata* L. (In Russian.) *Ent. Oboz.* **31**, 178.

KUENEN, D. J. (1946). Het fruitspint en zijn bestrijding. *Meded. Landb Voor-Dienst, Den Haag*, no. 44.

KUWANA, Z. (1932). Studies on the voltinism of the silkworm. *Jap. J. Zool.* **4**, (41), abstract no. 180.

KUWANA, Z. (1951). Temperature effect as a factor for the pupation of *Anthrenus verbasci* (Coleoptera, Dermestidae). (In Japanese, English summary.) *J. seric. Sci. Japan*, **20**, 202.

LATHROP, F. H. and NEWTON, R. C. (1933). The biology of *Opius melleus* Gahan, a parasite of the blueberry maggot. *J. Agric. Res.* **46**, 143.

LE BERRE, J-R. (1951). Hétérogéneité biologique des populations du criquet migrateur des Landes: *Locusta migratoria gallica* Rem. (Phasis transiens). *Rev. Zool. Agric. appl.* **10–12**, 1.

LE BERRE, J-R. (1953). Contribution à l'étude biologique du criquet migrateur des Landes (*Locusta migratoria gallica* Remaudière). *Bull. biol.* **87**, 227.

References

Lees, A. D. (1953a). Environmental factors controlling the evocation and termination of diapause in the fruit tree red spider mite *Metatetranychus ulmi* Koch (Acarina: Tetranychidae). *Ann. Appl. Biol.* **40**, 449.

Lees, A. D. (1953b). The significance of the light and dark phases in the photoperiodic control of diapause in *Metatetranychus ulmi* Koch. *Ann. Appl. Biol.* **40**, 487.

Lees, A. D. (1954). Unpublished observations.

Levenbook, L. (1951a). The variations in fat and glycogen content of the bot fly (*Gastrophilus intestinalis*) larva tracheal organ during development. *J. Exp. Biol.* **28**, 173.

Levenbook, L. (1951b). The effect of carbon dioxide and certain respiratory inhibitors on the respiration of larvae of the horse bot fly (*Gastrophilus intestinalis* de Geer). *J. Exp. Biol.* **28**, 181.

Ludwig, D. (1932). The effect of temperature on the growth curves of the Japanese beetle(*Popillia japonica* Newman.). *Physiol. Zoöl.* **5**, 431.

Ludwig, D. (1953). Cytochrome oxidase activity during diapause and metamorphosis of the Japanese beetle (*Popillia japonica* Newman). *J. Gen. Physiol.* **36**, 751.

MacDonald, S. and Brown, A. W. A. (1952). Cytochrome oxidase and cyanide sensitivity of the larch sawfly during metamorphosis. *83rd Ann. Rep. Ent. Soc. Ontario*, p. 30.

Maercks, H. (1934). Untersuchungen zur Ökologie des Kohlweisslings (*Pieris brassicae* L.). I. Die Temperaturreaktionen und das Feuchtigkeitoptimum. *Z. Morph. Ökol. Tiere*, **28**, 692.

Marchal, P. (1897). Les cecidomyies des céréales et leurs parasites. *Ann. Soc. ent. Fr.* **66**, 1.

Marchal, P. (1936). Recherches sur la biologie et le développement des Hyménoptères parasites: Les Trichogrammes. *Ann. Épiphyt.* **2**, 447.

Marikovsky, P. I. (1952). The tamarisk moth *Amblypalpis tamaricella* Dan. and the phenomenon of the linked diapause of its parasites. (In Russian.) *Zool. Zh.* **31**, 673.

Mathys, G. (1954). Contribution éthologique à la résolution du complex *Bryobia praetiosa* Koch (Acar., Tetranych.). *Mitt. schweiz. ent. Ges.* **27**, 137.

Matthée. J. J. (1951). The structure and physiology of the egg of *Locustana pardalina* Walk. *Bull. Un. S. Afr. Dep. Agric. Sci.* no. 316, 83 pp.

Mayet, V. (1896). Note sur *Margarodes vitium* Giard (Hém.). *Bull. Soc. Ent. Fr.* p. 50.

Mellanby, K. (1938). Diapause and metamorphosis of the blowfly, *Lucilia sericata* Meig. *Parasitology*, **30**, 392.

Muroga, H. (1951). On the consumption coefficient of inhibitory substance in silkworm eggs. (In Japanese, English title.) *J. Seric. Sci. Japan*, **20**, 92.

Nayar, K. K. (1953). *Schizomyia macarangae*, a new species of gall midge (Diptera: Itonididae). *Proc. Zool. Soc. Bengal*, **6**, 131.

Neiswander, C. R. (1947). Variations in the seasonal history of the European Corn Borer in Ohio. *J. Econ. Ent.* **40**, 407.

NORRIS, K. R. (1950). Aestivating eggs of the red-legged earth mite. *Bull. Coun. Sci Industr. Res. Aust.* no. 253, 26 pp.

O'KANE, W. C. and LOWRY, P. R. (1927). The European corn borer: life history in New Hampshire, 1923–1926. *Tech. Bull. N. H. Agric. Exp. Sta.* no. 33, 39 pp.

PAPPENHEIMER, A. M. and WILLIAMS, C. M. (1952). The effects of diphtheria toxin on the cecropia silkworm. *J. Gen. Physiol.* **35**, 727.

PAPPENHEIMER, A. M. and WILLIAMS, C. M. (1953). The properties of cytochrome *e* in the Cecropia silkworm. *Anat. Rec.* **117**, 543.

PARKER, J. R. (1930). Some effects of temperature and moisture upon *Melanoplus mexicanus mexicanus* Saussure and *Camnula pellucida* Scudder (Orthoptera). *Bull. Mont. Agric. Exp. Sta.* no. 223, 132 pp.

PARKER, M. W., HENDRICKS, S. B., BORTHWICK, H. A. and JENNER, C. E. (1952). Photoperiodic responses of plants and animals. *Nature, Lond.*, **169**, 242.

PARKER, H. L. and THOMPSON, W. R. (1927). A contribution to the study of hibernation in the larva of the European corn borer (*Pyrausta nubilalis* Hubn.). *Ann. Ent. Soc. Amer.* **20**, 10.

PEARSON, E. O. and MITCHELL, B. L. (1945). A report on the status and control of insect pests of cotton in the Lower River Districts of Nyasaland. Zomba, Nyasaland, Govt. Printer. 48 pp.

PEPPER, J. H. (1937). Breaking the dormancy in the sugar-beet webworm, *L. sticticalis* L., by means of chemicals. *J. Econ. Ent.* **30**, 380.

PEPPER, J. H. and HASTINGS, E. (1941). Life history and control of the sugar-beet webworm *Loxostege sticticalis* (L.). *Bull. Mont. Agric. Exp. Sta.* no. 389, 32 pp.

PETERSON, B. (1947). Die geographische Variation einiger Fennoskandischer Lepidopteren. *Zool. Bidr. Uppsala*, **26**, 329.

PETERSON, B. (1949). On the evolution of *Pieris napi* L. *Evolution*, **3**, 269.

PICKFORD, R. (1953). A two-year life-cycle in grasshoppers (Orthoptera: Acrididae) overwintering as eggs and nymphs. *Canad. Ent.* **85**, 9.

PICTET, A. (1913). Recherches expérimentales sur l'hibernation de *Lasiocampa quercus*. *Bull. Soc. lépidopt. Genève*, **2**, 179.

PREBBLE, M. L. (1941*a*). The diapause and related phenomena in *Gilpinia polytoma* (Hartig). I. Factors influencing the inception of diapause. *Canad. J. Res.* D, **19**, 295.

PREBBLE, M. L. (1941*b*). The diapause and related phenomena in *Gilpinia polytoma* (Hartig). II. Factors influencing the breaking of diapause. *Canad. J. Res.* D, **19**, 322.

PREBBLE, M. L. (1941*c*). The diapause and related phenomena in *Gilpinia polytoma* (Hartig). III. Bioclimatic relations. *Canad. J. Res.* D, **19**, 350.

PREBBLE, M. L. (1941*d*). The diapause and related phenomena in *Gilpinia polytoma* (Hartig.). IV. Influence of food and diapause upon reproductive capacity. *Canad. J. Res.* D, **19**, 417.

PREBBLE, M. L. (1941*e*). The diapause and related phenomena in *Gilpinia polytoma* (Hartig). V. Diapause in relation to epidemiology. *Canad. J. Res.* D, **19**, 437.

References

PRECHT, H. (1953). Über Ruhestadium erwachener Insekten. I. Versuche an Kartoffelkäfern (*Leptinotarsa decemlineata* Say). *Z. vergl. Physiol.* **35**, 326.

PUNT, A. (1950). The respiration of insects. *Physiol. comp.* **2**, 59.

RAHM, U. H. (1952). Die innersekretorische Steuerung der postembryonalen Entwicklung von *Sialis lutaria* L. (Megaloptera). *Rev. suisse Zool.* **59**, 173.

READIO, P. A. (1931). Dormancy in *Reduvius personatus* (Linnaeus). *Ann. Ent. Soc. Amer.* **24**, 19.

RICE, P. L. (1937). Effect of moisture on emergence of the ragweed borer *Epiblema strenuana* Walker, and its parasites. *J. Econ. Ent.* **30**, 108.

ROBBIE, W. A., BOELL, E. J. and BODINE, J. H. (1938). A study of the mechanism of cyanide inhibition: I. Effect of concentration on the egg of *Melanoplus differentialis*. *Physiol. Zoöl.* **11**, 54.

ROUBAUD, E. (1922). Sommeil d'hiver cédant à l'hiver chez les larves et nymphes de Muscides. *C.R. Acad. Sci., Paris*, **174**, 964.

ROUBAUD, E. (1928). Asthénobiose et hibernation obligatoire provoquées, chez *P. papatasii* Scop. *Bull. Soc. Path. exot.* **21**, 436.

ROUBAUD, E. (1930). Suspension évolutive et hibernation larvaire obligatoire provoquées par la chaleur chez le moustique commun *Culex pipiens* L. *C.R. Acad. Sci., Paris*, **190**, 324.

ROUBAUD, E. (1935). Vie latente et condition hibernale provoquées par les influences maternelles chez certains invertébrés. *Ann. Sci. nat.* **18**, 39.

ROUBAUD, E. and COLAS-BELCOUR (1926). La torpeur hivernale obligatoire et ses manifestations diverse chez nos moustiques indigènes. *C.R. Acad. Sci., Paris*, **182**, 871.

ROWLEY, R. R. (1923). Extended pupal duration. *Canad. Ent.* **55**, 198.

RUNNSTRÖM, J. (1930). Atmungsmechanismus und Entwicklungserregung bei den Seeigelei. *Protoplasma*, **10**, 106.

SABROSKY, C. W., LARSEN, I. and NABOURS, R. K. (1933). Experiments with light upon reproduction, growth and diapause in grouse locusts (Acrididae, Tetriginae). *Trans. Kansas Acad. Sci.* **36**, 298.

SACHAROV, N. L. (1930). Studies in cold resistance in insects. *Ecology*, **11**, 505.

SALT, G. (1932). The natural control of the sheep blow-fly, *Lucilia sericata* Meigen. *Bull. Ent. Res.* **23**, 235.

SALT, G. (1941). The effects of hosts upon their insect parasites. *Biol. Rev.* **16**, 239.

SALT, R. W. (1936). Studies on the freezing process in insects. *Tech. Bull. Minn. Agric. Exp. Sta.* no. 116, 41 pp.

SALT, R. W. (1947). Some effects of temperature on the production and elimination of diapause in the wheat stem sawfly, *Cephus cinctus* Nort. *Canad. J. Res.* D, **25**, 66.

SALT, R. W. (1949a). A key to the embryological development of *Melanoplus bivittatus* (Say), *M. mexicanus mexicanus* (Sauss.), and *M. packardii* Scudder. *Canad. J. Res.* D, **27**, 233.

SALT, R. W. (1949b). Water uptake in eggs of *Melanoplus bivittatus* Say. *Canad. J. Res.* D, **27**, 236.

Physiology of Diapause in Arthropods

SALT, R. W. (1952). Some aspects of moisture absorption and loss in eggs of *Melanoplus bivittatus* Say. *Canad. J. Zool.*, **30**, 55.

SALT, R. W. (1953). The influence of food on cold-hardiness of insects. *Canad. Ent.* **85**, 261.

SANBORN, R. C. and WILLIAMS, C. M. (1950). The cytochrome system in the cecropia silkworm, with special reference to the properties of a new component. *J. Gen. Physiol.* **33**, 579.

SCHMIEDER, R. G. (1933). The polymorphic forms of *Melittobia chalybii* Ashmead and the determining factors involved in their production (Hymenoptera: Chalcidoidea, Eulophidae). *Biol. Bull., Woods Hole*, **65**, 338.

SCHNEIDER, F. (1948). Beitrag zur Kenntnis der Generationsverhältnisse und Diapause rauberischer Schwebfliegen (Syrphidae, Dipt.). *Mitt. schweiz. ent. Ges.* **21**, 249.

SCHNEIDER, F. (1950). Die Entwicklung des Syrphidenparasiten *Diplazon fissorius* Grav. (Hym., Ichneum.) in uni-, oligo- und polyvoltinen Wirten und sein Verhalten bei parasitärer Aktivierung der Diapauselarven durch *Diplazon pectoratorius* Grav. *Mitt. schweiz. Ent. Ges.* **23**, 155.

SCHNEIDER, F. (1951). Einige physiologische Beziehungen zwischen Syrphidenlarven und ihren Parasiten. *Z. angew. Ent.* **33**, 150.

SCHNEIDERMAN, H. A. and WILLIAMS, C. M. (1953). The physiology of insect diapause. VII. The respiratory metabolism of the Cecropia silkworm during diapause and metamorphosis. *Biol. Bull., Woods Hole*, **105**, 320.

SCHNEIDERMAN, H. A. and WILLIAMS, C. M. (1954a). The physiology of insect diapause. VIII. Qualitative changes in the metabolism of the Cecropia silkworm during diapause and development. *Biol. Bull., Woods Hole*, **106**, 210.

SCHNEIDERMAN, H. A. and WILLIAMS, C. M. (1954b). The physiology of insect diapause. IX. The cytochrome oxidase system in relation to the diapause and development of the Cecropia silkworm. *Biol. Bull., Woods Hole*, **106**, 238.

SCHOLANDER, P. F., FLAGG, W., HOCK, R. J. and IRVING, L. (1953). Studies on the physiology of frozen plants and animals in the arctic. *J. Cell. Comp. Physiol.* **42**, suppl. 1, 1–56.

SEÇKIN, R. (1952). A study of the biology of *Cydia pomonella* in Amasya. (In Turkish.) *Bull. Plant Prot. (Ankara)*, no. 1, 29. Cited in *Rev. Appl. Ent.* A (1952), **40**, 222.

SELLIER, R. (1949). Diapause larvaire et macroptérisme chez *Gryllus campestris* (Ins. Orth.). *C.R. Acad. Sci., Paris*, **228**, 2055.

SHAPPIRIO, D. G. and WILLIAMS, C. M. (1953). Cytochrome E in individual tissues of the Cecropia silkworm. *Anat. Rec.* **117**, 542.

SHELFORD, V. E. (1929). *Laboratory and Field Ecology.* Baltimore: Williams and Wekins.

SIMMONDS, F. J. (1948). The influence of maternal physiology on the incidence of diapause. *Phil. Trans.* B, **233**, 385.

SLIFER, E. H. (1930). Insect development. I. Fatty acids in the grasshopper egg. *Physiol. Zoöl.* **3**, 503.

References

SLIFER, E. H. (1931). Insect development. II. Mitotic activity in the grass-hopper embryo. *J. Morph.* **51**, 613.

SLIFER, E. H. (1932). Insect development. IV. External morphology of grasshopper embryos of known age and with known temperature history. *J. Morph.* **53**, 1.

SLIFER, E. H. (1938). The formation and structure of a special water-absorbing area in the membranes covering the grasshopper egg. *Quart. J. Micr. Sci.* **80**, 437.

SLIFER, E. H. (1946). The effects of xylol and other solvents on diapause in the grasshopper egg; together with a possible explanation for the action of these agents. *J. Exp. Zool.* **102**, 333.

SLIFER, E. H. (1948). Isolation of a wax-like material from the shell of the grasshopper egg. *Disc. Faraday Soc.* no. 3, 182.

SLIFER, E. H. (1949). Changes in certain of the grasshopper egg coverings during development, as indicated by fast green and other dyes. *J. Exp. Zool.* **110**, 183.

SLIFER, E. H. (1950). A microscopical study of the hydropyle and hydro-pyle cells in the developing egg of the grasshopper *Melanoplus differentialis. J. Morph.* **87**, 239.

SLONIMSKI, P. P. (1953). A specific relation between enzymic adaptation and cytoplasmic mutation. In 'Adaptation in micro-organisms'. *3rd Symp. Soc. Gen. Microbiol.* pp. 76–94. Cambridge University Press.

SMITH, O. J. and LANGSTON, R. L. (1953). Continuous laboratory propaga-tion of Western Grape Leaf Skeletonizer and parasites by prevention of diapause. *J. Econ. Ent.* **46**, 477.

SQUIRE, F. A. (1939). Observations on the larval diapause of the pink bollworm, *Platyedra gossypiella* Saund. *Bull. Ent. Res.* **30**, 475.

SQUIRE, F. A. (1940). On the nature and origin of the diapause in *Platyedra gossypiella*, Saund. *Bull. Ent. Res.* **31**, 1.

STANDFUSS, M. (1896). *Handbuch der Paläarktischen Gross-Schmetterlinge für Forscher und Sammler*, 2nd ed. Jena: Fischer.

STEELE, H. V. (1941). Some observations on the embryonic development of *Austroicetes cruciata* in the field. *Trans. R. Soc. S. Aust.* **65**, 329.

STEENBURGH, W. E. VAN (1929). Laboratory rearing of *Laspeyresia molesta. Sci. Agric.* **9**, 616.

STEINBERG, D. M. and KAMENSKY, S. A. (1936). Les prémisses oecologiques de la diapause de *Loxostege sticticalis* L. (Lepidoptera, Pyralidae). *Bull. biol.* **70**, 145.

STRELNIKOV, I. (1936). Wasserumsatz und Diapause bei *Loxostege sticticalis. C.R. Acad. Sci. U.R.S.S.* (N.S.), **1**, no. 6, 267.

SÜFFERT, F. (1924). Bestimmungsfaktoren des Zeichnungsmuster beim Saison-Dimorphismus von *Araschnia levana-prorsa. Biol. Zbl.* **44**, 173.

TANAKA, Y. (1924). Maternal inheritance in *Bombyx mori. Genetics*, **9**, 479.

TANAKA, Y. (1944). Effect of daylength on hibernation of the Chinese oak silkworm. (In Japanese.) *Agric. Hort. (Nōgyō oyobi Engei)*, **19**, no. 9.

Physiology of Diapause in Arthropods

TANAKA, Y. (1950*a*). Studies on hibernation with special reference to photoperiodicity and breeding of the Chinese Tussar-silkworm. I. (In Japanese.) *J. Seric. Sci. Japan*, **19**, 358.

TANAKA, Y. (1950*b*). Studies on hibernation with special reference to photoperiodicity and breeding of the Chinese Tussar-silkworm. II. (In Japanese.) *J. Seric. Sci. Japan*, **19**, 429.

TANAKA, Y. (1950*c*). Studies on hibernation with special reference to photoperiodicity and breeding of the Chinese Tussar-silkworm. III. (In Japanese.) *J. Seric. Sci. Japan*, **19**, 580.

TANAKA, Y. (1951*a*). Studies on hibernation with special reference to photoperiodicity and breeding of the Chinese Tussar-silkworm. V. (In Japanese.) *J. Seric. Sci. Japan*, **20**, 132.

TANAKA, Y. (1951*b*). Studies on hibernation with special reference to photoperiodicity and breeding of the Chinese Tussar-silkworm. (In Japanese.) *J. Seric. Sci. Japan*, **20**, 191.

TANAKA, Y. (1953). Genetics of the silkworm, *Bombyx mori*. *Advanc. Genet.* **5**, 239.

TATE, P. and VINCENT, M. (1936). The biology of autogenous and anautogenous races of *Culex pipiens* L. (Diptera: Culicidae). *Parasitology*, **28**, 115.

THEODOR, O. (1934). Observations on the hibernation of *Phlebotmus papatasii* (Dipt.). *Bull. Ent. Res.* **25**, 459.

THERON, P. P. A. (1943). Experiments on terminating the diapause in larvae of codling moth. *J. Ent. Soc. S. Afr.* **6**, 114.

THOMSEN, E. (1952). Functional significance of the neurosecretory brain cells and the corpus cardiacum in the female blow-fly *Calliphora erythrocephala* Meig. *J. Exp. Biol.* **29**, 137.

THORPE, W. H. (1929). Biological races in *Hyponomeuta padella* L. *J. Linn. Soc. (Zool.)*, **36**, 621.

TOWNSEND, M. T. (1926). The breaking-up of hibernation in the codling moth larva. *Ann. Ent. Soc. Amer.* **19**, 429.

TOYAMA, K. (1912). On certain characteristics of the silkworm which are apparently non-Mendelian. *Biol. Zbl.* **32**, 593.

TULESCHKOV, K. (1935). Über Ursachen der Überwinterung der *Lymantria dispar, L. monarcha* und anderer Lymantriiden im Eistadium. *Z. angew. Ent.* **22**, 97.

UMEYA, Y. (1926). Experiments of ovarian transplantation and blood transfusions in silkworms, with special reference to the alternation of voltinism (*Bombyx mori* L.). *Bull. Seric. Exp. Sta. Chosen*, **1**, 1.

UMEYA, Y. (1950). Studies in embryonic hibernation and diapause in insects. *Proc. Imp. Acad. Japan*, **26**, no. 6, 1.

USHATINSKAYA, R. S. (1952). Trends in certain physiological processes in the body of insects in the prehibernation period. (In Russian.) *Bull. Acad. Sci. U.R.S.S.* Biol. Ser., no. 1, 101.

UVAROV, B. P. (1931). Insects and Climate. *Trans. R. Ent. Soc. Lond.* **79**, 1.

VANCE, A. M. (1939). Occurrence and responses of a partial second generation of the European corn borer in the Lake States. *J. Econ. Ent.* **32**, 83.

References

VANCE, A. M. (1942). Studies on the prevalence of the European corn borer in the East North Central States. *Circ. U.S. Dep. Agric.* no. 649, 23 pp.

VARLEY, G. C. and BUTLER, C. G. (1933). The acceleration of development of insects by parasitism. *Parasitology*, **25**, 263.

WALOFF, N. (1949). Observations on larvae of *Ephestia elutella* Hübner (Lep. Phycitidae) during diapause. *Trans. R. Ent. Soc.* **100**, 147.

WAY, M. J. and HOPKINS, B. A. (1950). The influence of photoperiod and temperature on the induction of diapause in *Diataraxia oleracea* L. (Lepidoptera). *J. Exp. Biol.* **27**, 365.

WHEELER, W. M. (1893). A contribution to insect embryology. *J. Morph.* **8**, 1.

WIESMANN, R. (1950). Untersuchungen über die Diapause der Puppe der Kirschfliege *Rhagoletis cerasi* L. *Mitt. schweiz. ent. Ges.* **23**, 207.

WIGGLESWORTH, V. B. (1934). The physiology of ecdysis in *Rhodnius prolixus* (Hemiptera). II. Factors controlling moulting and 'metamorphosis'. *Quart. J. Micr. Sci.* **77**, 191.

WIGGLESWORTH, V. B. (1936). The function of the corpus allatum in the growth and reproduction of *Rhodnius prolixus* (Hemiptera). *Quart. J. Micr. Sci.* **79**, 91.

WIGGLESWORTH, V. B. (1948). The functions of the corpus allatum in *Rhodnius prolixus* (Hemiptera). *J. Exp. Biol.* **25**, 1.

WIGGLESWORTH, V. B. (1952). Hormone balance and the control of metamorphosis in *Rhodnius prolixus* (Hemiptera). *J. Exp. Biol.* **29**, 620.

WIGGLESWORTH, V. B. (1954). *Metamorphosis in Insects.* Cambridge University Press.

DE WILDE, J. (1949). Het experimenteel beinloeden van het verloop der generaties bij de Coloradokever (*Leptinotarsa decemlineata* Say). *Bijdr. Dierk.* **28**, 543.

DE WILDE, J. (1953). Provisional analysis of the imaginal diapause in an insect (*Leptinotarsa decemlineata* Say). *Acta physiol. pharm. néerl.* **3**.

WILLIAMS, C. M. (1946). Physiology of insect diapause: the role of the brain in the production and termination of pupal dormancy in the giant silkworm *Platysamia cecropia*. *Biol. Bull., Woods Hole*, **90**, 234.

WILLIAMS, C. M. (1947). Physiology of insect diapause. II. Interaction between the pupal brain and prothoracic glands in the metamorphosis of the giant silkworm, *Platysamia cecropia*. *Biol. Bull., Woods Hole*, **93**, 89.

WILLIAMS, C. M. (1948). Extrinsic control of morphogenesis as illustrated in the metamorphosis of insects. *Growth Symp.* **12**, 61.

WILLIAMS, C. M. (1952a). Physiology of insect diapause. IV. The brain and prothoracic glands as an endocrine system in the cecropia silkworm. *Biol. Bull., Woods Hole*, **103**, 120.

WILLIAMS, C. M. (1952b). Morphogenesis and the metamorphosis of insects. *Harvey Lecture*, 1951–2.

WISHART, G. (1947). Further observations on the changes taking place in the corn borer population in Western Ontario. *Canad. Ent.* **79**, 81.

WOLSKY, A. (1938). The effect of carbon monoxide on the oxygen consumption of *Drosophila melanogaster* pupae. *J. Exp. Biol.* **15**, 225.

WOLSKY, A. (1949). The physiology of development in insects. *Proc. Nat. Inst. Sci. India*, **15**, 67.

YAKHIMOVICH, L. A. (1950). Changes in the environmental requirements of the Asiatic locust during embryonic development. (In Russian.) *C.R. Acad. Sci. U.R.S.S.* (N.S.), **73**, no. 5, 1105.

ZHUKOVSKY, A. V. (1950). The diapause of the larvae of the Hessian fly. (In Russian.) *Doklady Vsesoyuz. Akad. sel.-khoz. Nauk Lenina*, **15**, no. 6, 26.

ZOLOTAREV, E. KH. (1947). Diapause and development of pupae of the Chinese oak silkworm (*Antheraea pernyi* Guer.). (In Russian.) *Zool. Zh.* **26**, 539.

ZOLOTAREV, E. KH. (1950). The development of the larvae of the hawthorn butterfly (*Aporia crataegi* L.) in the winter period. (In Russian.) *Zool. Zh.* **29**, 152.

ZOLOTAREV, E. KH. and POPEL, Y. A. (1947). On the nature and duration of embryonic diapause in the mulberry silkworm (*Bombyx mori* L.). (In Russian.) *Doklady Vsesoyuz. Akad. sel.-khoz. Nauk Lenina*, **12**, no. 7, 33.

INDEX

Index

Index

Polychrosis, 17, 33, 37, 124
Polypedilum, 78–9
Popillia, 6, 98
Pristophora, 98
prothoracic glands, 107, 110
Pyrausta, 31, 45, 53, 75, 80, 114, 130–1

Quadrivoltine strains, 44
quiescence, 2

Receptor mechanisms, 40
Reduvius, 6
reproductive diapause, 110–11
respiration, 90–8
respiratory quotient, 93
reversal of taxes, 18
Rhagoletis cerasi, 66
R. completa, 59
R. pomonella, 83
Rhodnius, 101, 110, 112
Rhopobata, 9
Rhynchites, 78
Rothschildia, 59

Saissetia, 82
saliva, 82, 86
Saturnia, 54
Scelio, 81
Schizomyla, 78
Sciara, 78
Scoliopterix, 88
selection experiments, 47–9
sensitive periods, 32–6, 60–3
short-day species, 16
Sialis, 7, 107, 110
Sitodiplosis, 60, 81
Smerinthus ligustri, 56
S. ocellatus, 56, 93
Sminthurus, 77
Spalangia, 36, 39, 114

Spilosoma, 16
spiracles, 120
Sturmia, 81
suboesophageal ganglion, 102–4, 118
synchronous growth of insects and plants, 131–2
synchronous growth of parasites and hosts, 80–6
Syrphus, 78, 82

Telea, 31, 33, 46
Telenomus, 56
temperature and diapause induction, 6, 29–32, 41, 43–4, 123–6, 129–30
temperature and diapause termination, 54–64, 109–10, 122, 127–8, 131–2
temperature optima, 50–2
Tetranychus, 17, 128
Theophila, 9
threshold of illumination, 19
Timarcha tenebricosa, 10, 56, 89
T. violacea-nigra, 10
token stimuli, 13
Trichogramma, 84–5
Trypoxylon, 38

Voltinism, 5

Water conservation during diapause, 120
water content during diapause, 68–76, 88
water content of food, 38
water uptake, 69–79
wax layers, 71, 120
winter eggs, 12
wound stimuli, 66, 72, 86

Xiphidium, 2
xylol treatment, 66, 71–2